Merry Christmas Jeannie 1974
from
Pawpaw & Snomaw. We

Adventures in Fact

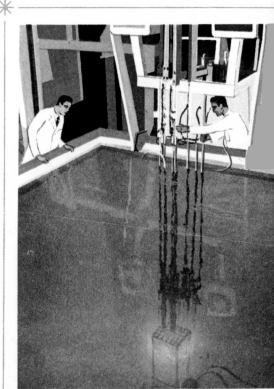

Adventures in Fact

THE WALT DISNEY PARADE
OF FUN, FACT, FANTASY AND FICTION

WITH ILLUSTRATIONS BY THE WALT DISNEY STUDIO

Golden Press ✳ New York

Contents

Photographs for "Fishes of the Tropical Atlantic" and "Fishes of the Indian and Pacific Oceans" by A. van den Nieuwenhuizen; drawings by P. Gofferje. From "Wonders of the Ocean" © 1967.

Our Friend The Atom

Foreword

FICTION often has a strange way of becoming fact. Not long ago we produced a motion picture based on the immortal tale 20,000 *Leagues under the Sea*, featuring the famous submarine "Nautilus." According to that story the craft was powered by a magic force.

Today the tale has come true. A modern namesake of the old fairy ship—the submarine "Nautilus" of the United States Navy—has become the world's first atom-powered ship. It is proof of the useful power of the atom that will drive the machines of our atomic age.

The atom is our future. It is a subject everyone wants to understand, and so we long had plans to tell the story of the atom. In fact, we considered it so important that we embarked on several *atomic projects*.

For one, we are planning to build a Hall of Science in the TOMORROWLAND section of DISNEYLAND where we will—among other things—put up an exhibit of atomic energy. Then, our *atomic projects* at the Walt Disney Studios were two-fold: we produced a motion picture and this book, so that we could tell you this important story in full detail. Both grew together. Many

illustrations appear in both, and we gave them the same title: *Our Friend the Atom.*

With our *atomic projects* we found ourselves deep in the field of nuclear physics. Of course, we don't pretend to be scientists—we are story tellers. But we combine the tools of our trade with the knowledge of experts. We even created a new Science Department at the Studio to handle projects of this kind. The story of the atom was assigned to Dr. Heinz Haber, Chief Science Consultant of our Studio. He is the author of this book and he helped us in developing our motion picture.

The story of the atom is a fascinating tale of human quest for knowledge, a story of scientific adventure and success. Atomic science has borne many fruits, and the harnessing of the atom's power is only the spectacular end result. It came about through the work of many inspired men whose ideas formed a kind of chain reaction of thoughts. These men came from all civilized nations, and from all centuries as far back as 400 B.C.

Atomic science began as a positive, creative thought. It has created modern science with its many benefits for mankind. In this sense our book tries to make it clear to you that we can indeed look upon the atom as our friend.

Prologue

Deep in the tiny atom lies hidden a tremendous force. This force has entered the scene of our modern world as a most frightening power of destruction, more fearful and devastating than man ever thought possible.

We all know of the story of the military atom, and we all wish that it weren't true. For many obvious reasons it would be better if it weren't real, but just a rousing tale. It does have all the earmarks of a drama: a frightful terror which everyone knows exists, a sinister threat, mystery and secrecy. It's a perfect tale of horror!

But, fortunately, the story is not yet finished. So far, the atom is a superb villain. Its power of destruction is foremost in our minds. But the same power can be put to use for creation, for the welfare of all mankind.

What will eventually be done with the atom? It is up to us to give the story a happy ending. If we use atomic energy wisely, we can make a hero out of a villain.

This, then, is the story of the atom. It is a story with a straightforward plot and a simple moral almost like a fable. In many ways the story of the atom suggests the famous tale from the *Arabian Nights*: "The Fisherman and the Genie." Perhaps this tale even hints at what lies in our atomic future. . . .

There once *lived an aged Fisherman, who dwelt in poverty with his wife and three children. Each day he cast his net into the sea four times, and rested content with what it brought forth.*

One day, after three vain casts, the old Fisherman drew in his net for the fourth time. He found it heavier than usual. Examining his catch, he found among the shells and seaweeds a small brazen vessel. On its leaden stopper was the ancient seal of King Solomon.

"A better catch than fish!" he exclaimed. "This jar I can sell. And who knows what thing of value it might contain?"

With his knife he pried out the stopper. Then, as he peered into the jar, smoke began to pour from it. He fell back in astonishment as the smoke rose in a great dark column and spread like an

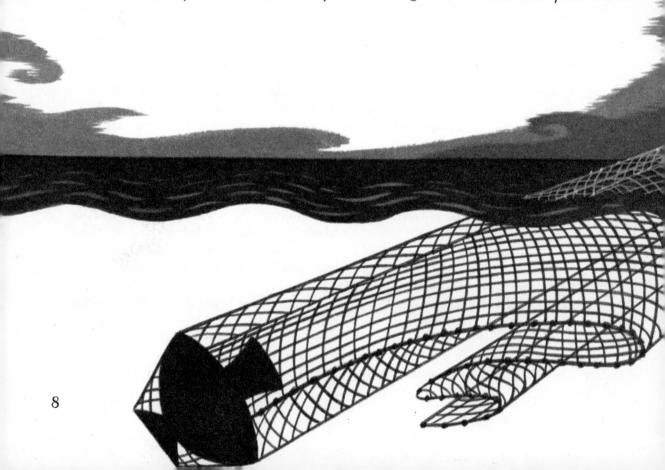

enormous mushroom between earth and sky. And his astonishment turned into terror as the smoke formed into a mighty Genie, with eyes blazing like torches and fiery smoke whirling about him like the simoom of the desert.

"Alas!" cried the old Fisherman, falling to his knees. "Spare me, O Genie. I am but a poor man, who has not offended thee!"

The Genie glared down on the trembling old man.

"Know," he thundered, "that because thou hast freed me, thou must die. For I am one of those condemned spirits who long ago disobeyed the word of King Solomon. In this brazen vessel he sealed me, and he commanded that it be cast into the sea, there to lie forever—or until some mortal should, by unlikely chance, bring up the vessel from the depths and set me free."

The old Fisherman listened in silent fear as the Genie's eyes flamed.

"For centuries," the great voice of the Genie continued, "I lay imprisoned deep in the sea, vowing to grant to my liberator any wish—even to make him master of all the wealth in the world, should he desire it. But no liberator came. At last, in my bitterness, I vowed that my liberator, who had delayed so long, should have no wish granted him—except how he should die. Thou, old man, art my liberator, and according to my solemn vow thou must die!"

"O," wailed the Fisherman, "why was I born

to set thee free? Why did I cast this net and bring forth from the deeps this accursed vessel? Why must thou reward me with death?"

The fiery smoke swirled more swiftly about the Genie, and he gestured with impatience.

"Fisherman," he roared, "delay not, but choose how thou wilt die!"

The old Fisherman was terrified indeed. Yet in this moment of danger he was able to bestir his wits.

"O Genie," he begged, "if I must die, so be it. But first grant me this one wish. Thy great form did seem to come forth out of this little vessel, and yet I cannot believe it. Prove to me that one who is so mighty can indeed fit into such a little vessel."

The Genie towered above the little fisherman. His eyes blazed brighter.

"Old man," he thundered, "thou shalt see, before thy death, that nothing lies beyond my powers."

Swiftly the Genie dissolved into smoke, and the smoke funneled back into the little vessel.

Instantly the Fisherman leaped forward and thrust the leaden stopper, bearing the seal of King Solomon, into the jar.

"Now," he shouted to the imprisoned Genie, "choose how thou, in thy turn, wilt die! A prisoner thou art again, and back into the depths will I fling thee. All fishermen, and their children, and their children's children, shall be warned of the

10

wicked Genie and forbidden ever to cast their nets here. And at the bottom of the sea shalt thou lie forevermore!"

The Genie's agitated voice sounded faintly through the brazen vessel. "Stop, stop! Only set me free once more, and thou shalt live!"

The Fisherman raised the vessel to cast it into the waves. "O Genie," he said, "only when I cast thee back into the sea shall I be safe."

The voice in the little vessel grew frantic. "Fisherman, hear me! Live thou shalt, and richly! Restore my freedom and I vow, by Allah, to grant thee three wishes, to make thee rich and happy all thy days. Good Fisherman, hear my solemn vow!"

The old man had little heart for revenge, and he bethought himself of what a friendly Genie might do for his ragged, hungry family. The Genie continued to entreat him for mercy. And at last the Fisherman pried out the stopper.

Once more the smoke poured forth, and again the giant form of the Genie loomed against the sky. With a great kick, the Genie sent the brazen vessel spinning far out over the waves.

The old Fisherman trembled, fearing the worst. But the Genie turned toward him, and bowed his towering form, and spoke gently.

"Fear not," he said. "You heard my vow. O Fisherman, my master, name thy three wishes. . . ."

THIS FABLE tells of the age-old wish of man to be the master of a mighty servant that does his bidding. But to us it has a still deeper meaning: the story of the atom is like that tale; we ourselves are like that fisherman. For centuries we have been casting our nets into the sea of the great unknown in search of knowledge. Finally a catch was made: man found a tiny vessel, the atom, in which lies imprisoned a mighty force—atomic energy.

Like the fisherman, man marveled at his strange find and examined it closely for its value. He pried it open—split it in two. And as he did so a terrible force was released that threatened to kill with the most cruel forms of death: death from searing heat, from the forces of a fearful blast, or from subtly dangerous radiations.

And as it was to the fisherman, it is to us a great, an almost unbelievable marvel that such a tremendous force could dwell in such a tiny vessel.

Here we are, we fishermen, marveling and afraid, staring at the terrifying results of our curiosity. The fable, though, has a happy ending; perhaps our story can, too. Like the Fisherman we must bestir our wits. We have the scientific knowhow to turn the Genie's might into peaceful and useful channels. He must at our beckoning grant three wishes for the good of man. The fulfillment of these wishes can and will reshape our future lives.

So this is our story: how the atomic vessel was discovered, how man learned of its many marvelous secrets, how the atomic Genie was liberated, and what we must do to make him our friend and servant.

Atoms Everywhere

ONE DAY in August 1945 the world suddenly became conscious of the atom. This was the beginning of what is now known as the "atomic age." Before that day, the atom had led a rather obscure and quiet life in the textbooks of physics and chemistry, and nobody except scientists cared much about it. Many people didn't even know of the atom's existence—until that day in 1945 when a frightful flash burned the word "atom" into the mind of modern man.

Like the vessel the Fisherman of our fable had found, the atom had lain in the sea of the unknown for a long time. In fact, the atom had been in existence long before man himself, and even before the birth of the earth on which he lives. For eons the atom had been the chief actor on the stage on which the drama of the universe is in continuous performance.

Everything around us is entirely composed of atoms: the paper of the book you are reading,

the table in front of you, your house, the trees—yourself, and the very air you breathe. Everything is composed of those absolutely invisible, extremely small particles.

Because atoms are so very small, their number must be extremely large. Consider how many atoms there are in a breath of air. Under normal conditions a human being inhales and exhales about one pint of air with every breath. This means that about 16 times in every minute you are inhaling and exhaling no less than 25,000,000,-000,000,000,000,000 atoms!

The number of atoms in a breath of air is 25 with 21 zeros. This number is so big that it doesn't have a simple name. We use a composite name: twenty-five thousand billion billion.

There is no way of grasping such big numbers. Only a few technical people are used to dealing with them. A number of this size must be broken down if we want to bring it closer to our understanding. Let's try this with an example—an example based on a wild idea.

Leonardo da Vinci, the famous artist and scientist of the Italian Renaissance, was 67 years old when he died in 1519. During these 67 years of his life he was breathing about 16 times in every minute, at the rate of about 25,000,000,000,000,000,000,000 atoms a breath. In his lifetime he must have pumped a tremendous grand total of atoms through his lungs. Now then, is there a chance that every once in a while you, in the twentieth century, inhale an atom that once passed through the lungs of Leonardo da Vinci?

The answer is this: In every single breath of yours there are no less than 2 billion atoms that were once breathed by this great man!

This is a fabulous, almost frightening result, but it is substantially true. The entire air of the earth has undergone thorough mixing since Leonardo's time. Storms, updrafts, hurricanes, trade winds have carried Leonardo's atoms all over the earth in all directions. Of course, Leonardo didn't breathe a whole new set of atoms with every new breath; in closed rooms, for example, he often re-breathed atoms that had been in his lungs once or even many times before. To be on the safe side, therefore, let's say that in each breath of Leonardo's only one out of 20 atoms was one that never before had been in his lungs. Even so, with every breath you take today, you inhale 100 million atoms that were once breathed by Leonardo da Vinci!

This example is possible only because atoms are permanent and indestructible. The few exceptions are so rare that we can disregard them here absolutely. So the atoms once breathed by

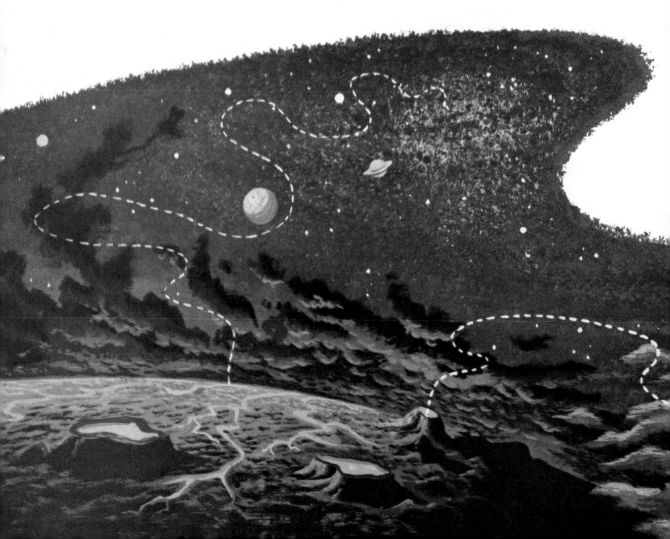

Leonardo still exist. They are all around us in great numbers. And, of course, these atoms existed a long time before Leonardo's century. Being once in the lungs of this great man was just one insignificant event in the long life of one of these atoms—one single event in its life of billions of years.

Like other atoms, this atom was probably created between 4 and 5 billion years ago. Many scientists believe that all atoms of which the planets, stars, and galaxies are built were created in a giant explosion that took place this long ago. Our atom was probably among them. For countless millions of years it drifted through the vast spaces of the universe. In the course of time, galaxies, stars, and planets formed. Our atom became part of a giant whirlpool of dust and gas that later was to develop into our solar systems. In this whirlpool full of smaller whirlpools our atom eddied around and around—thousands of millions of times. It still keeps whirling around, even today. For our atom got caught in a stream of matter that became part of the earth, and, as everyone knows, the earth spins around its own axis, and at the same time it swings around the sun. Our atom, being part of this planet, still keeps whirling along at a dizzying pace.

Originally, our atom was caught inside the earth's crust. It rested there for millions of years

before it reached the surface. Finally it was spewn forth from the depths in a prehistoric eruption of a volcano. Since that time it has spent most of its time in the air. Every so often it has lodged in the body of some kind of life form, only to be released back into the air after a period of captivity. More than 450 years ago it happened to drift around the city of Florence, Italy, and Leonardo da Vinci inhaled it. After a short while the atom was again expelled, and once more it began to tumble around all over the planet. Right now it happens to be close to you, and you are about to inhale it with your next breath.

What a history! But there is one more thing to be said about that atom—something even more marvelous than the countless numbers and almost unbelievably small size of the atoms that make up the universe. Our atom, like every other one, holds a secret—the secret of a tremendous force hidden in its tiny body. This energy is the Genie of our fable.

The release of the atomic Genie has been one of the most momentous achievements in the history of Western man. The achievement itself has had a long history. Before scientists learned of the energy of the atom, they had to find out about its parts and its architecture. And before this, the atom had to be discovered. No easy task, considering its smallness!

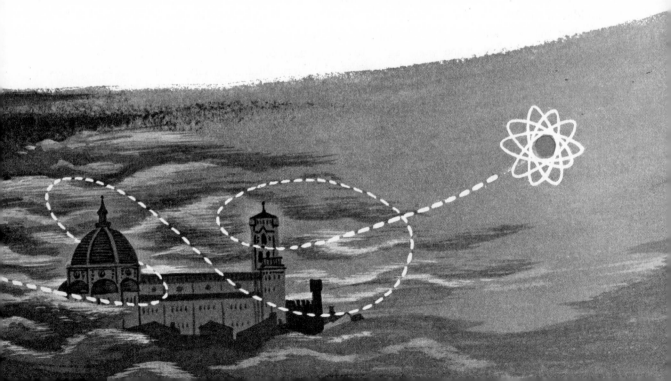

The Smallest Particle

KNOWLEDGE of the atom is something that belongs to our own time. It is a new and modern thing; the atom meant little or nothing to people who lived only a generation ago. But actually the idea of the atom is quite old—amazingly old. The first man we know of who thought of the atom lived more than 2,300 years ago. He belonged to a group of philosophers who, centuries before the birth of Christ, began to reason about the world around them. They were the famous philosopher-scientists of ancient Greece.

Before these men were born, it was thought that everything in the world was the work of gods, genies, and demons of all kinds. Most were obviously quite unfriendly, and man looked upon them with awe and superstition. The Greek thinkers, however, began to reason systematically. They refused to be frightened by superstition. They used logic and tried to understand and explain Nature and her laws. In fact, these philoso-

phers were the very first who reasoned that there is such a thing as a law of Nature that a reasoning mind can detect and understand.

This enlightened period in the history of man began with the great Thales of Miletus, a city in Asia Minor. Thales was one of the first of the Greek philosopher-scientists. During his lifetime he traveled a good deal, and at one time he must have conferred with Babylonian astronomers who were diligent observers of the skies. Thales inspected their tables, in which had been faithfully recorded all eclipses of the sun and the moon that had been observed since thousands of years before their time. Like all peoples in this age, the Babylonians had a fancy explanation for these eclipses. They thought that a huge dragon resided in the sky, and every once in a while this frightful creature would almost swallow the sun or the moon, or at other times would obscure these heavenly lights in the awful coils of its tail. Not so Thales. The story goes that he knew that these eclipses returned at certain regular inter-

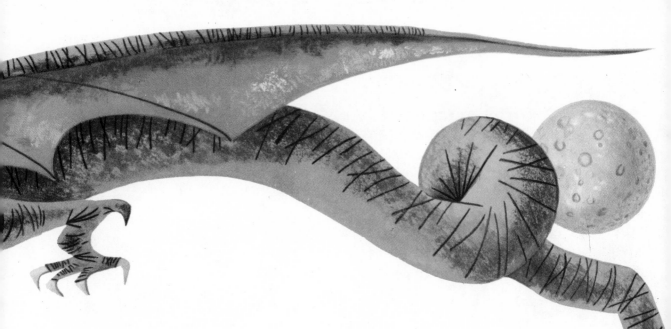

vals; we don't know if he found this out by himself, or if his Babylonian friends told him. Whatever happened, Thales didn't believe the story of the dragon—he reasoned that eclipses are a natural phenomenon. And so he began to draw conclusions: since eclipses had occurred regularly in the past, they must recur in the future with the same regularity. After a thorough inspection of the Babylonian tables, he predicted that another eclipse of the sun was due on May 28, 585 B.C. Quite understandably to us moderns, the eclipse took place on that very day.

Probably there were others who performed similar feats: the Mayas of ancient Mexico, astronomers of old China, and even the Babylonians themselves. Some correct predictions were probably made even before Thales was born, but of these we will never know. Exact data go back only to ancient Greece, and so we can say that the light of reason began to shine for the first time when the light of the sun was blotted out temporarily by the moon.

Around 465 B.C., about 80 years after the death of Thales, the philosopher Democritus was born in Abdera, a little town in Thrace, a province of ancient Greece. To the best of our knowledge, Democritus was the first to think of the atom. Some historians believe that still another philoso-

pher, Leucippus, had the idea of the atom as early as 500 B.C.; but Democritus of Abdera went far beyond expressing just an idea. He developed a full atomic theory which later turned out to be a fabulously clear foresight of many detailed facts discovered by modern science. Democritus has justly been called the father of the atom.

We don't know how Democritus explained his atomic theory to his disciples. In those days, discourse and argument were a great art, and each philosopher had a number of devoted students. The ancient Greeks loved to walk while they indulged in their arguments. So Democritus sometimes might have led his students to the coast of the Mediterranean for a demonstration of his ideas. He might have picked up a clod and said:

"Look here, if I crumble this clod in my hands, I get smaller clods. Now I rub one of these smaller clods between my fingers, and what I get is fine dust. Let's inspect this dust on my fingers more closely. It consists of small particles that we can barely see. Next, I rub this dust still more, with the result that my fingers become powdery. This powder must also consist of small particles—too small for the human eye to see.

"Now, I contend that these tiny pow-

ΔΕΜΟΚΡΙΤΟΣ

der particles can be rubbed down to still smaller ones, and these, in turn, can be reduced further to yet smaller particles. If I go on in this fashion, I shall finally come to an end. Then I shall have reduced matter to its smallest particles, which cannot be broken down any further. These smallest, indivisible particles I call 'atoms.' "

It was Democritus who gave us the word "atom"; that is, he used the Greek word *atomos*, which means something that cannot be cut.

"See," Democritus might have continued, "how this beach appears to be a solid carpet. But on closer inspection we see that it is composed of millions of grains of sand. If we think of grains of sand as atoms and pack them together, they can be molded into any desired form.

"It is in this way that Nature uses her atoms to build all things . . . the earth—the water—air and fire."

Democritus saw the universe as a vast void in which the atoms reside. The atoms themselves are thought to be created eternally; they are indestructible and of indivisible hardness. They are absolutely full and incompressible. The atoms themselves remain forever unchanged; but through their incessant motion and ever-changing arrangements among themselves they weave the colorful tapestry of the physical world.

Then Democritus might have explained the nature of solid metals, the liquid water, the gaseous air. Such was his remarkable insight into the true nature of things.

There are many different kinds of atoms, Democritus told his students: little smooth spheres, sharp-edged cubes, and irregular ones with rough surfaces. If a mass of rough atoms are packed together closely, they will stick to each other, and it becomes almost impossible to tear them apart. This would explain the toughness of metals, and why most of them can be cut only with great difficulty.

Other atoms are smooth and heavy, like highly polished balls of steel. If they are heaped upon each other in great numbers, they begin to slide freely over one another because there is hardly any friction between them. This mass of atoms would then be fluid, like—water! This would explain the heaviness of water and, at the same time, it would account for its easy fluidity.

Again, other kinds of atoms are both light and smooth. They float about freely, moving constantly in all directions. A large mass of such atoms would give us the fleeting air and the wavering flames of fire.

When he envisioned his atoms, there was one thought foremost in the mind of Democritus. The atoms themselves stood for permanence and eternal stability. They represented a universal, unchanging law of nature. But there was also everlasting change in the world of atoms. They were ever active, rearranging themselves in new designs and patterns, only to break up again in search of new arrangements. This everlasting change included man himself. Democritus taught that a human being undergoes constant change: when he breathes he inhales new atoms which become fixed in his body, replacing others that are expelled with the air he exhales. In this way man himself becomes part of the everlasting change that makes the world.

All these thoughts and explanations are truly prophetic. With a few small qualifications the theories of Democritus can serve as an excellent introduction to a book on modern atomic physics or chemistry.

Despite their brilliant clarity, the ideas of Democritus became lost, or almost so. His writings vanished, and only a few fragments of his teachings were relayed through the centuries. But there was another reason why the atomic theory of Democritus was forgotten, and stayed forgotten for a long, long time. This reason was Aristotle.

The philosopher Aristotle was born in the year 384 B.C., when Democritus was still alive. Aristotle did not believe in the existence of the atom. He used, instead, arguments of the following sort:

"If air and fire consisted of small, solid particles—how could they rise? They would fall to the earth like pebbles!"

To explain the nature of the universe, Aristotle used simple elements. Unlike the atoms, the basic elements of Aristotle were visible to the eye and noticeable to the touch. To him there were four qualities: hot, cold, moist, and dry. Earth, for example, was cold and dry, water was cold and moist, air was hot and moist, and fire was hot and dry. If something was moist, it was so not because it contained atoms of a liquid as Democritus had taught; to Aristotle something was moist simply because it contained "moisture."

These explanations were disarmingly simple and compelling. Hot, cold, moist, and dry—earth, water, air, and fire: these were homely, everyday terms that did not require any abstract thinking like Democritus' atoms. Aristotle explained things by themselves—their true nature could be seen and felt.

Such was the basis of the philosophy of Aristotle. Of course, the whole system of his thoughts was complicated enough, but the premises of his philosophy were simple and appealing. His ideas governed the mind of man for almost 2,000 years.

Democritus and his atoms were forgotten.

New Vistas

THE YEAR was 1589. A young man, barely 25 years old, was appointed professor of mathematics at the University of Pisa, Italy. He was paid a yearly salary of 60 scudi—a little more than 50 dollars. He didn't last through his three-year appointment. He left before his time was up, but not because he felt underpaid. He decided to leave before his colleagues ran him out of town. His name was Galileo Galilei.

The reason why Galileo aroused the ire of the whole faculty was simple: he didn't live up to the rules. Immediately after his appointment he began to tell his students that Aristotle and his teachings were amiss. If we explain wetness by saying that it is wet, he argued, then we shall never discover the true nature of things. He refused to accept the theories of Aristotle at face value, as his colleagues had done for centuries. The philosophy of Aristotle already was more than 1,900 years old, and for this reason alone it had to be respected. But Galileo decided to make his own investigation of things, and what he saw with his own two eyes inspired him to fight for his ideas. It was to be a long fight, and it lasted through the 78 years of his rich life.

Galileo was convinced that a scientist must go beyond mere thinking. He must also act, and so Galileo did. A famous law of nature formulated by Aristotle, for example, stated that heavy things fall faster than light ones. This appeared more than plausible to everyone. And it was considered perfectly easy to demonstrate the truth of this "law"; just drop an iron ball and a bird's feather, and see for yourself!

Galileo thought this classical example was too obvious. So, according to his account, he took an iron "bomb" weighing 100 pounds, and an iron cannon ball weighing only half a pound. According to Aristotle the bomb ought to fall 200 times faster than the cannon ball. Galileo wanted to prove that this simply wasn't so. He hauled the two objects to the topmost story of the Leaning Tower of Pisa and dropped them from this overhanging vantage point. He released the two objects at exactly the same time. Both the bomb and the cannon ball tore into the ground, the bomb leading the ball by less than the breadth of a finger. They had been falling at practically the same speed. The little difference Galileo attributed to the action of air resistance—which, incidentally, also explains why the feather falls slowly. In a complete vacuum a feather drops like a rock.

This experiment exemplifies the kind of tests to which Galileo put prevailing ideas. Galileo started a mode of thinking which is still in use today. Since Galileo we have decided open questions in science by observation and experimentation.

Even though he was eminently successful with his first experiments, Galileo could not convince his colleagues that Aristotle must have been wrong. But his experiments were the beginning of the end of the domination of man's thinking by untested ideas. Man now went actively after

new discoveries, and Aristotle, though still respected as a philosopher, became discredited as a physical scientist.

In writing about science it is difficult to get away from Galileo. Even though this great man probably never used the word "atom" in all his life, we must stay with him for a while in our story of the atom. With his further work he did much to open the eyes and minds of the scientists that came after him. Unknowingly, he prepared the ground for a revival of Democritus' ideas.

In about 1609 Galileo made a simple telescope and directed it at the sky. The telescope had been recently invented by a Dutch spectacle maker, Hans Lippershey, but when Galileo first held one in his hands he did not indulge in the pastime of making a distant church steeple appear much closer. To him, the telescope was not a toy but a scientific instrument. He used it for making those things come closer that man himself could not approach.

Within an incredibly short time, during 1609 and 1610, he made a whole series of truly sensational astronomical discoveries. His fame spread through all of Europe after he announced that there were mountains on the moon and that the sun sometimes showed spots. He discovered the four largest moons of Jupiter and observed with

delight how these small satellites swung around the mighty planet just as, he was convinced, the earth and the other planets swing around the sun. He saw in this spectacle a small model of the solar system. He detected the rings of Saturn, although the poor power of his telescope would not reveal the whole beauty of this unique phenomenon in our solar system. He discovered that the planet Venus, our lovely morning and evening star, showed phases like the moon.

Often he must have pointed his small telescope at the Milky Way where its soft star clouds are brightest. There, through his telescope, the silvery shine of the Milky Way resolved itself into the twinkling of thousands and thousands of stars that no man's eye had ever seen. Never before had so much of our galaxy—a cloud of billions of stars in measureless space—been viewed by the human eye.

In 1610 Galileo published a famous book in which he told of his exciting discoveries. He aptly titled it THE STAR MESSENGER, and it did contain a message:

> "There is a vast universe all around us, filled with countless moons, planets, and stars—an outer space in which earth and man are lost as small, insignificant parts."

1670

AT about the same time another important instrument was invented—the microscope. It, too, was probably invented in Holland, but nobody can tell with certainty who its inventor was. Many scientists of that time built microscopes after the principle had become known. Actually invented before the telescope, the microscope remained a toy for almost a century, until the Dutchman Antony Leeuwenhoek used it for research. In many ways, Leeuwenhoek matched the feat of Galileo with the telescope. Leeuwenhoek, too, made a whole series of new discoveries when he began to use the microscope in 1670. But the microscope could not duplicate the sensation which the telescope had caused. Leeuwenhoek, for one thing, was not nearly so famous as Galileo, and also somehow people are more easily impressed by things big than by things too small for the eye to see.

Yet Leeuwenhoek's discoveries were truly spectacular. Before his eyes unfolded an entirely new world, full of strange patterns and designs. He found them in the crystalline structures of metals, in wood, in snowflakes. He discovered order and beauty in the colorful wings of butterflies and bees, and in the filigree of miniature sea shells.

Galileo had taught scientists to go after new discoveries with an open mind. In this spirit Leeuwenhoek searched further. And he became the first man to see really tiny forms of life—little, one-celled animals that nobody dreamed existed.

Man had for a long time only his own two eyes to use when he went out in search of new things. Then suddenly, in the seventeenth century, he built himself two magic eyes that enlarged the weak powers of his sight many hundred times. With these magic eyes he discovered the vastness of outer space and he saw the unbelievable smallness of inner space.

As late as 1580, a professor or student of the University of Oxford used to be fined five shillings every time he made a statement or used an argument contrary to the teachings of Aristotle. Before man could discover outer and inner space, Galileo and other scientists had to break down the prestige of Aristotle. Of course, the microscope could not show the atoms of Democritus. But it made man aware of hitherto invisible things, and soon he began to reason that small things must be composed of something still smaller. . . .

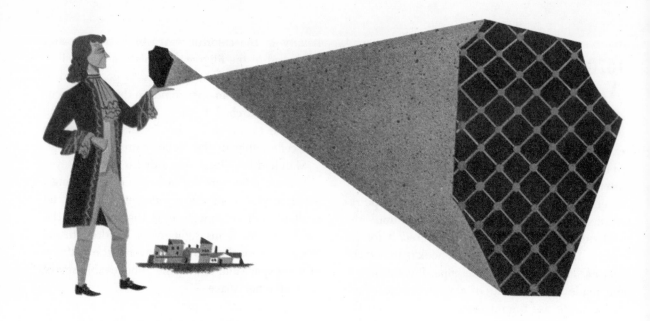

The Secret of Matter

GALILEO, the founder of our modern science, taught us how to make Nature yield her secrets. He asked shrewd questions in the form of experiments, and Nature herself gave the answers. This new way of research also included theory, the method of finding a result by sheer reasoning. Since Galileo, science has used theory and experiments as a powerful pair of tools to solve tough problems. Theory and experiment are like the two arms of a nutcracker: a nut cannot be cracked easily with just one lever.

The story of the atom shows this clearly. It was a long and tortuous road that was to lead to the discovery of the atom. The fisherman had to cast his net many, many times. . . .

In the beginning there were no experiments that would detect atoms. A scientist could not take a piece of metal or wood and cut it into smaller and smaller pieces until he had separate atoms. The atom is so hopelessly small that it lies forever beyond the crude touch of human hands and beyond the dim sight of human eyes, even if aided by the most powerful microscope. So, when the atom emerged for the second time during the history of science, it did not appear as the result of an experimental study; as happened the first time, somebody just thought of it. It entered the scene of modern science as a pure theory.

We owe the revival of the atomic theory to a man who, like Democritus himself, was more a philosopher than a scientist: Pierre Gassendi, of France. He was born in 1592, and sixteen years later was already a teacher of rhetoric in his home town of Digne, France. At the age of only nineteen he was offered a position to teach philosophy in the village of Aix in southern France. Like Galileo, Gassendi disputed Aristotle, and in his early twenties he wrote a biting dissertation in which he exposed the fallacies of the ancient master's philosophy. His manuscript was so sarcastic that his friends advised him to moderate it, because Aristotle was still in high esteem with the most influential scholars of that time. Gassendi's works were finally published in 1658, three years after his death. They could no longer do harm to him then.

The atomic theory of Gassendi is not much different from that of Democritus. Probably Gassendi had knowledge of the ideas of the old thinker; but he added a few of his own. He thought that atoms of solid bodies must possess small hooks that would interlock to form strong networks like those of metal bedsprings. In this way, Gassendi thought, solid materials like metals and rocks are given their toughness and hardness. He gave much thought to this problem of how atoms could stick together. At one place in his writings he even claimed that there is a force acting between all atoms that makes them hold on to each other like so many small magnets.

With this concept of a "magnetic" attraction between atoms, Gassendi was verging on a theory of physics. This might be the reason why the great physicist Sir Isaac Newton, discoverer of the law of gravitation, was much interested in the books of Gassendi. Newton, too, believed in atoms. He even thought that light rays are composed of a fast stream of extremely small particles that flow away in all directions from a source of light such as a candle. To Newton all things—solid bodies, liquids, gases, and even intangible light—were composed of atoms. At one time he wrote the following:

"It seems probable to me, that God in the Beginning form'd Matter in solid, massy, hard, impenetrable, moveable Particles, of such Sizes and Figures, and with such other Properties, and in such Proportion, as most conduced to the End for which He form'd them; and that these primitive Particles being Solids, are incomparably harder than any porous Bodies compounded of them; even so very hard as never to wear or break

Newton thought even light is made up of particles.

in Pieces, no ordinary Power being able to divide what God Himself made one in the first Creation."

Naturally, all this was theory. Newton expressed this clearly when he began his statement with the words: "It seems probable to me. . . ." The experimental proof of the atom's existence still lay a long time in the future.

Matter had now to be studied—matter, the visible and tangible stuff of which everything is made. For in matter lies the atom.

What kinds of matter are there? There are so many kinds that they are hard to classify. The ancient philosophers had their simple system: they spoke of the four elements—earth, water, air, and fire. All matter below their feet was earth: rock, sand, clay, and all metals that lay buried in the ore. The ocean, lakes, and rivers consisted of water, the atmosphere of air, and the sun was built of fire. There is hardly any worthwhile information in this crude system—just enough so that Democritus and Gassendi could speculate about atoms sticking together to form the solid earth, just enough to tell that atoms of liquids are slippery, and atoms of gases are free to fly about.

This system of the four elements was confusing in many ways. What if water froze and became solid ice? Was it still water or did it become earth when it froze hard? What if a piece of gold was thrown into a red-hot crucible, where it melted and started to flow like water? Did it become water when it became fluid? No, the ancient elements lead into a dead-end road. Before they were removed from the thinking of science, there could be scant progress. So, when Robert Boyle, of England, entered the scientific scene, he cast aside the old four elements.

Unlike Galileo and Gassendi, Boyle was a rich man. He was born in 1627, son of the Earl of Cork. At the age of eight, Robert was sent to Eton, and later to France, Switzerland, and Italy. After the death of his father he inherited a considerable fortune. To him science was, so to speak, a hobby. He must have found it quite absorbing, because he never found the time to marry.

In 1661 he published a book under the title *The Sceptical Chemist*. It was a good title, for the book advised his colleagues in chemistry to clear their minds of the mystery and black magic contained in the old writings. Most of the books Boyle attacked had been written by the old alchemists, who searched for the secret of making gold from lesser metals like lead or iron. Boyle was convinced that gold could not be "made"; it was something only Nature could create. It could not be found in the green flasks of a magician unless it had been put there in the first place. To Boyle, gold was an "element," by which

he meant that it was a basic substance that could not be composed of or made from other substances. He taught that some other kinds of matter—copper, silver, and the strange fluid mercury—were also elements.

Boyle was convinced that all the different kinds of matter, which the ancients found so confusing, could be reduced to a much smaller number of such basic substances. There are many kinds of houses, all different in size, style, and appearance, but all can be reduced to bricks, pipes, beams, rafters; such are the elements of a house. But just as the composition of a house can be "analyzed" to consist of bricks, pipes, beams, and rafters, Boyle thought that more complicated kinds of matter like clay, salt, or glass could be understood

as being composed of two or more elements. Their build-up could be found by "chemical analysis." All this sounds simple today, but when Boyle applied his idea of the element to the chemistry of his time, it was a great feat.

More than a century had to pass before Boyle's idea of the chemical element brought science one step closer to the atom. Again we must go to France; this time to Antoine Laurent Lavoisier.

This great chemist was an extremely active man. He was tall, handsome, and an acute thinker. It was he who brought order and rule into chemistry, which before him was little more than a disorganized play of cooking, boiling, and mixing according to all kinds of fancy recipes. Lavoisier began to weigh and to measure. Applying his scales shrewdly, he soon cleared up one of the great chemical mysteries of his time: he explained what happens when something burns.

A very superficial observation shows that things lose weight when they burn. When you shove a log into the fireplace, it is heavy. Then it begins to burn, slowly it falls apart, and after a while it shrinks to a small heap of ashes. The ashes are so light and fluffy that you could blow them away.

Actually, things *gain* weight when they are burned! A burning piece of wood develops a lot of smoke, vapors, gases, soot, and ashes. If all these could be collected, their combined weight would be greater than that of the original log. This is a rather unexpected result. It takes a clear mind like that of Lavoisier to expect what most people would not expect. He took a piece of the chemical element sulfur, weighed it accurately, then burned it under carefully controlled conditions so that the resulting smoke and vapor could be weighed. When he did weigh them, they turned out to be heavier than the original sample of the sulfur.

On November 1, 1772, Lavoisier sent a sealed envelope to the secretary of the French Academy of Sciences. The envelope contained a note describing in a few sentences what he had observed. Lavoisier also promised that some time later he would publish a detailed account of his experiments. He sealed this note in an envelope so that later, if challenged, he could prove to everyone that he was the first to discover the chemical principles of combustion.

What happened to the sulfur was simply this: in burning, the element sulfur combined with the element oxygen in the air. This combination occurred in what is called a chemical reaction between the two elements. The smoke and vapors, of course, had to be heavier than the sulfur alone, because oxygen had been added to the sulfur while it burned.

With his scales Lavoisier had looked into the nature of a chemical reaction more deeply, more knowingly than any chemist before him. He could prove with precise measurements that Nature builds matter by combining different elements.

Lavoisier recognized that the chemical element is of great importance to the understanding of the nature of matter. He spent much effort on the elements themselves. He compiled the first list of elements—a total of 28. A hundred years before his time there were assumed to be only 4; today we know over a hundred.

The great Lavoisier met with a tragic death. In May 1794, during the French Revolution, he was arrested on the trumped-up charge that he had mixed water into the tobacco of the soldiers. The Revolutionary Tribunal sentenced him to die on the guillotine. During his trial he pointed to the many services he had rendered his country during his active life as a scientist. The judge cut him short: "The Republic doesn't need scientists!" He was executed within 24 hours.

Later the famous French mathematician Lagrange bitterly remarked, "It took them but a moment to sever that head, though a hundred years, perhaps, will be required to produce another like it!"

After Lavoisier, scientists knew that everything around us consists somehow of chemical elements. These combine and mix in certain ways to produce the colorful variety of all kinds of matter— solid, liquid, and gaseous. Democritus and Gassendi had spoken of atoms in the same terms. Obviously, chemical elements and atoms somehow must be related.

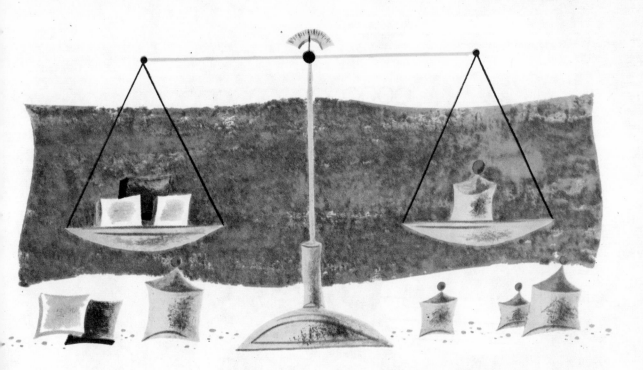

Patterns

Tʜᴇ ᴊᴜᴅɢᴇs of the French Revolutionary Tribunal could kill Lavoisier, but they could not kill his work. He was the first to use a scale in his laboratory, and the chemists who came after him continued to weigh and measure.

It wasn't long before the chemical scale revealed a great and important secret about matter and about how Nature mixes her elements. Actually, it turned out that "mixing" wasn't quite the right word.

There is such a thing as a true mixture. We can mix sugar and sand so thoroughly that it would be practically impossible to separate them again. They can be mixed in any amounts and in any proportions.

But there are other kinds of "mixtures" that work only in certain ways. Suppose you want a checkerboard pattern of tiles on a floor—alternating black and red squares. For this pattern the "mixture" of the black and red tiles is to be 1 to 1. Suppose all the tiles are to weigh 120 pounds; then, when the tile man comes, he should bring 60 pounds of black tiles and 60 pounds of red ones. If he brings 50 pounds of black tiles and 70 pounds of red ones, he will wind up with 20 pounds of red tiles too many for the job. The checkerboard pattern demands an exact mixture.

There are many other kinds of mixtures. Consider a floor to be made of tiles in a pattern that is arranged in such a manner that each blue tile is surrounded by eight yellow tiles. This pattern takes three times as many yellow tiles as blue ones. To lay such a floor, a tile man will bring 30 pounds of blue tiles and 90 pounds of yellow tiles. Here the tiles will mix only in a 3-to-1 ratio, just as the checkerboard allowed only 1 red tile to 1 black one.

Now we see that the word "mixture" isn't quite right if it comes to regular patterns as in tile floors. A mixture of sugar and sand is a true mixture. In laying a floor, however, we find that tiles fall naturally into a pattern; they join in a regular fashion. If it comes to patterns that are regular, we would do better to speak of "compounds" rather than mixtures.

Now, around 1800 there were many chemists conducting countless chemical experiments in their laboratories. They weighed and measured.

These scientists found that some elements did indeed mix in any desired amounts. They simply fell together like so many handfuls of sugar and sand. But most elements behaved differently. When they were put together, they didn't simply mix—they combined in a chemical reaction such as Lavoisier had shown for combustion. And most elements did combine only in certain, fixed amounts. It was discovered, for example, that 46 ounces of sodium always combined with 71 ounces of chlorine to produce 117 ounces of table salt. Similarly, 1 ounce of hydrogen would only combine with 8 ounces or oxygen to produce exactly 9 ounces of water. If 2 ounces of hydrogen were mixed with 8 ounces of oxygen, 1 ounce of hydrogen was left over.

For a number of years these chemists were busy with their scales, their minds set on finding out how many ounces of one element would combine with how many ounces of another element. They published long tables of these combination weights. Their work was very important, but somehow they did not fully realize what was emerging—not until, in 1808, the great English physicist and chemist John Dalton showed them.

John Dalton was born a poor country boy. He came from a Quaker family, and from his early youth he had to look out for himself. As a young boy he worked on the farm, but he soon found that he could earn his livelihood with his clever little head much better than with his hands. At the age of only twelve he started to teach school in the village, and only three years later he became an assistant teacher at a boarding school. At nineteen he was made principal of that school, and in the course of the following years he

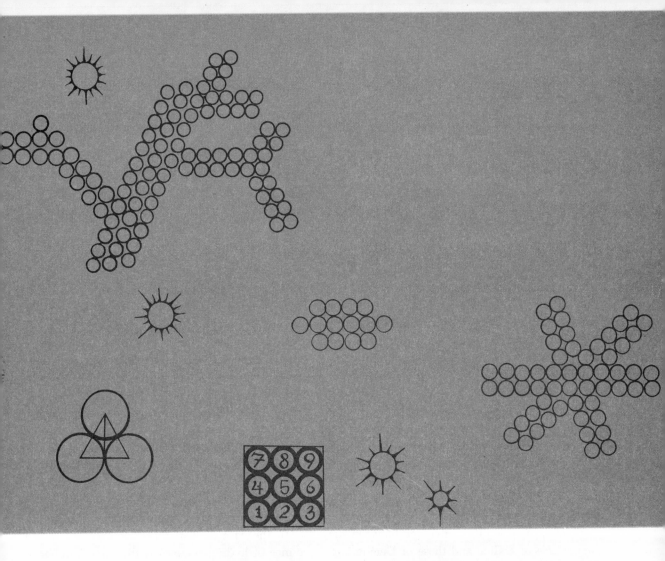

studied Latin, Greek, French, mathematics, and natural sciences. The rest of his life was spent teaching in English universities.

Dalton did all his eminent research in physics and chemistry in his free time. He was mostly interested in physics and meteorology. Only at the age of about forty did he direct his attention to chemistry.

He was fascinated by the way in which Nature combines her elements to form the many different compounds that were already known in his time. There was this remarkable law that elements combined only in certain proportions. He was the first who recognized this law in all its striking clarity and he lifted it out of the tables which the chemists had written up.

And then suddenly he realized that this wonderful law could only be explained by the atom.

And so Dalton began to design his famous atomic theory of chemistry. He claimed that matter consists of atoms, and that there exists an unknown force that acts between atoms to hold them together. He even drew pictures of his atoms—little dots and circles with rays indicating the forces of attraction acting between them. He also drew pictures of how atoms group together to form larger pieces of matter. Copper atoms, for instance, group together in little regular squares. When many atoms group together in this fashion, they form large sheets of atoms laid out in a regular checkerboard-type pattern. If millions of such sheets are packed upon each other—layer upon layer, and millions upon millions—they will form a tiny crystal visible under a microscope. If millions of these crystals combine, they form the copper metal that is familiar to us.

31

Just as there are atoms of copper, there are other kinds of atoms—one particular kind of atom for each chemical element. Since Dalton we have known that there are atoms of hydrogen, of oxygen, of iron, copper, mercury, and all the other chemical elements. All atoms of one particular element are absolutely alike. Two atoms of oxygen, for example, are more alike than two identical twins. If they were visible, nobody could tell them apart. They have the same shape and size, and above all, they weigh exactly the same. Atoms of another element are different; they have a different weight from oxygen; but among themselves they are again absolutely alike.

Actually, there is little difference between the atomic ideas of Dalton and those of Democritus, Gassendi, and Newton. All these ideas were theories and assumptions that nobody could really prove. After all, if something is too small to be visible, then you can claim just about everything about it. Nobody can prove you wrong—but neither can you prove that you are right. But Dalton was the first who had something to show in favor of his atomic theory, something that was not available to the old masters.

For one thing, there was the regular form of crystals. Dalton explained their striking regularity through the regular patterns in which atoms are supposed to be arranged. It was no direct proof of the atom, though. The microscope did show that even very tiny crystals had the same regular and orderly forms as big ones; but no microscope can actually show single atoms. It was impossible to prove that the crystal patterns really go back to regular arrangements of single atoms. This was an excellent idea, and today we know that Dalton was right; but at that time there was no way of testing his idea.

But Dalton advanced a second, stronger point in favor of his atomic theory. By this theory he explained why most elements mix only in certain fixed amounts, as 1 ounce of hydrogen with 8 ounces of oxygen to form 9 ounces of water. Said Dalton: 1 ounce of hydrogen and 8 ounces of oxygen consist of two groups of individual atoms, just as two stacks of tiles consist of individual tiles. When the groups combine, they arrange themselves in a certain pattern.

In the case of water, Dalton assumed that 1 ounce of hydrogen contains the same number of atoms as 8 ounces of oxygen. When 9 ounces of water are formed from these ingredients, each hydrogen atom joins one oxygen atom to form a pair—just as our tile man matched black and white tiles. In both cases—atoms as well as tiles—all units are used up because each finds a partner.

If each atom of hydrogen is represented by the symbol H, and each oxygen atom by the symbol O, then the chemical combination of the two can be written as follows:

$$H \quad + \quad O \quad = \quad HO$$
$$(1 \text{ ounce}) \quad (8 \text{ ounces}) \quad (9 \text{ ounces})$$

According to Dalton, the symbol "HO" then stood for one atom of water.

This idea was the stroke of a genius. It brought man to grips with the invisible atom.

But—there was still something not quite right!

The Case of the Missing Clue

THE YEAR was 1808, and a momentous year it was. For we know today that when Dalton designed his atomic theory, he all but solved the riddle of how chemical elements combine to form chemical compounds. He was the first to express the idea that atoms of different elements stick together and form small, compound particles.

We say "all but solved"—because Dalton did not know how many atoms of each element formed any given compound. He had not one solution for the riddle but many—and he didn't know which was right.

It was a situation of the sort that happens in detective stories. There were a number of clues, pointing to different solutions; but there weren't enough clues to tell which was the right solution. In his water problem, for example, Dalton had assumed that there were as many atoms in 1 ounce of hydrogen as in 8 ounces of oxygen. That gave him 1 hydrogen atom for each oxygen atom in his water recipe. But what if 1 ounce of hydrogen contained only half as many atoms as there are in 8 ounces of oxygen? He would then have 2 oxygen atoms for each hydrogen atom in his recipe, and the water formula would be HOO or HO_2!

At this point his atomic theory was up against a certain type of problem which has been known to scientists for centuries. It was first described by the Greek mathematician Diophantus, who lived in Alexandria, Egypt, around A.D. 260. To this day a problem of this type is known under the name of "Diophantine Equation." In keeping with the lingo of the detective story we could say that Dalton was dealing with the "case of the missing clue."

Here is a simple example of a Diophantine equation: A farmer goes to town and sells 2 piglets and 4 turkeys. When he comes home he has 24 dollars, and the question is how much money he got for each of his 4 turkeys. Of course, this problem cannot be solved the way it is given. It has many solutions, and you wouldn't know which solution is the right one. For example, our farmer could have got 2 dollars for each of his turkeys, if he received 8 dollars for each of his piglets. Or, if he got 6 dollars for each piglet, we would know that he sold his turkeys for 3 dollars each. This problem has as many solutions as you want. It can only be solved if one more clue is given, such as the price for one piglet. Then the right solution can be found at once.

Fortunately for Dalton, the missing clue was found within three years of the first publication of his atomic theory. The information was sup-

plied in the form of a marvelous law of Nature discovered by the Italian physicist Amadeo Avogadro.

Like many physicists of his time, Avogadro was very much interested in gases and how they behaved under different conditions of pressure and temperature. Since the time of Galileo, scientists had known that gases, trapped in a cylinder or closed vessel, are elastic, like springs. The air trapped inside a pump is a clear example. When you close the air outlet with a finger and push the piston handle, it is as though you were working against a coil spring. In fact, air—being a gas—is such an excellent spring that we use it in our automobile tires to get a soft, springy ride.

Since Galileo, physicists had been experimenting with this interesting springiness or pressure of air and other gases. In the course of time they had found that gases followed a set of rather simple rules. One of these gas laws had been discovered by Robert Boyle, the man who showed what a chemical element is. This law, known as "Boyle's law," was first published by him in a paper entitled "On the Spring of the Air." It simply stated that a mass of gas trapped in a vessel doubles its pressure if it is compressed to half the space it occupied before. Conversely, the pressure of a gas is reduced in proportion as the volume of the enclosing vessel is increased.

Other gas laws were found after Boyle's time. These have to do with the temperature of gas. We all know, for example, that the pressure in automobile tires increases after a car is driven for a while and the tires get hot. These gas laws involving temperature were discovered only a few years before Dalton and Avogadro concentrated their efforts on the atom.

For many years Avogadro was professor of physics at the University of Turin, Italy. In 1811 he discovered the law that, ever since, has been linked to his name:

If gases of any kind, having the same pressure and temperature, are put into vessels of equal size, the vessels contain the same number of gas particles.

Hydrogen and oxygen, for instance, can be put into ordinary gallon bottles. The law of Avogadro states that the number of atoms found in each bottle will be the same at the same pressure and the same temperature. The law would also hold for nitrogen and chlorine, two other gases.

Avogadro had the missing clue, and he proceded at once to use it on Dalton's problem. All he had to do was to look up in the tables of the chemists how much a gallon of hydrogen and how much a gallon of oxygen did weigh. The table showed that a gallon of oxygen was 16 times heavier than a gallon of hydrogen. But in each gallon there was the same number of atoms: so an oxygen atom must be 16 times heavier than a hydrogen atom! It was a simple, but very important, result.

The rest was easy. Since oxygen atoms are 16 times heavier than hydrogen atoms, one would have the same number of atoms in ½ ounce of hydrogen as in 8 ounces of oxygen. But Dalton's water recipe called for a whole ounce of hydrogen to 8 ounces of oxygen; hence in the water recipe there must be 2 hydrogen atoms to every oxygen atom. When they combined in a chemical reaction, they formed "H_2O"—water!

Dalton had shown how chemical compounds are formed: atoms of different elements stick together and form what he called "compounded atoms." Avogadro showed how many atoms of each kind go into each compounded atom. He was also the first to see how important these compounded atoms are for the understanding of physics and chemistry. He even gave them a name of their own so that there was a clear distinction between these compounded atoms and single ones. He called the compounded atoms "molecules," which means "little masses." The name "atom" he reserved for the single, ultimate particles which make up a chemical element.

The formation "H_2O" is a molecule, according to Avogadro; it is a water molecule, the smallest water particle. If a mass of these molecules are thrown together—millions and billions of them— then we get a drop of water.

There are also molecules that consist of two or more atoms of the same kind. Oxygen, as we find it in the air all around us, is composed of small particles in which two oxygen atoms are joined like two ping-pong balls glued together. The same is true for hydrogen. If three oxygen atoms join together to make one molecule, we get ozone, a poisonous gas.

Now everything became clear. Chemical elements are composed of single atoms, or of molecules in which the same kind of atoms are glued together. Chemical compounds consist of molecules in which there are two or more different kinds of atoms.

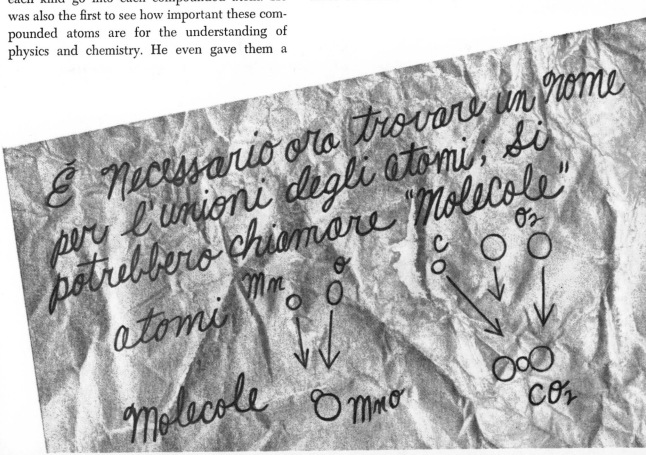

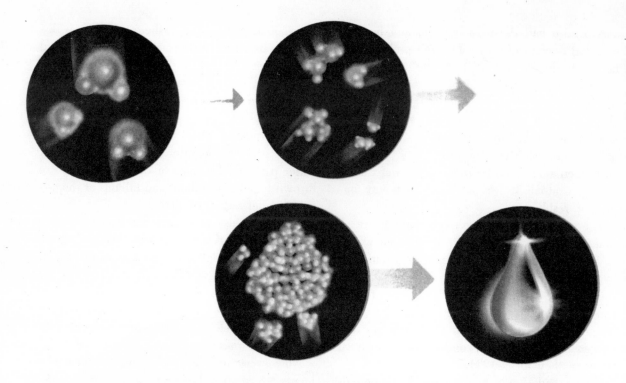

After Avogadro had completed his work, the atomic theory of Dalton was finally accepted. Today we look upon Dalton as the father of the modern atom, and in Avogadro we see the father of the molecule.

A tremendous task remained to be done, however. It fell upon the chemists to find out how the many molecules in Nature are built—how many atoms of a kind are found in them. It became a fascinating game of numbers and combinations to solve these many questions. It was like a huge crossword puzzle that grew faster than it could be solved.

The game started with simple molecules such as are formed when sodium and chlorine atoms combine. Both these elements are highly poisonous. But when a sodium atom (Na) and a chlorine atom (Cl) join to form the simple molecule "NaCl," we get nothing else but . . . table salt. Then more complicated molecules were tackled. For example, 12 atoms of carbon (C), 22 atoms of hydrogen (H), and 11 atoms of oxygen (O) may join in a certain way to form a molecule, $C_{12}H_{22}O_{11}$, which is nothing but—sugar.

Chemists of today are still busy finding out how atoms join to form molecules. All the simple molecules have long since been analyzed; today chemists wrestle with molecules that consist of tens of thousands—even hundreds of thousands—of single atoms! Such are the molecules of which the living bodies of plants, animals, and humans are built. In 1955, Dr. Linus Pauling, of the California Institute of Technology, received the Nobel Prize in Chemistry for his study of these giant molecules.

Avogadro used his marvelous law to find out how much heavier an oxygen atom is than a hydrogen atom. The same thing can be done with all other kinds of atoms. In this way chemists found out about the so-called "atomic weights." Hydrogen turned out to be the lightest of all atoms, and so it was given an atomic weight of 1. Oxygen then has the atomic weight 16, iron 56, and the heaviest of all is uranium, 238.

Nobody has ever seen a single atom, even to this day. At the time of Avogadro many scientists still thought there was no such thing as an atom. But only a few years later it was generally known how heavy the atom of each known element is in relation to a hydrogen atom.

Atoms at Work

Aɴᴅ so, more than a hundred years ago, scientists were already hot on the trail of the atom. Hardly a single reputable scientist remained who was not convinced that the atom exists; all believed in the atom, though nobody had ever seen one. Yet the belief in its existence was based entirely on what a lawyer would call circumstantial evidence.

It was as though the atom was the defendant in a trial. The judge, the jury, and the witnesses were all scientists. The witnesses brought to court a tremendous number of observations from the scene of the crime, and these facts could only be explained if there was such a thing as an atom. The jury weighed the facts. The circumstances were such that it could only conclude: the atom exists. A defense counsel could only have said: "Gentlemen—all this is only circumstantial evidence. Nobody has ever found a trace of an atom, nothing like a fingerprint. Nobody has ever seen the atom in action!" But the jury found the atom guilty of being in existence.

At last, in 1827, a witness did see the atom in action. This was real evidence observed with a microscope. One day the English botanist, Robert Brown, was looking at a drop of water with the highest power that his microscope could provide. There was in the water a number of very small specks of dust and some tiny bits of microscopically small plants. Brown didn't know what these little bits actually were, but he thought they were alive. They trembled, vibrated, and danced around without ever stopping. He believed they were creatures much smaller than the one-celled animals and plants known in his time. And so he misunderstood the evidence.

Only 52 years later, in 1879, was this "Brownian movement" given its correct explanation. The tiny bits of dust moved because they were constantly being kicked around by the everlasting motion of the water molecules. It was as though Brown had looked upon an anthill from the top of a high tree. He was too high above the scene of action to recognize the thousands of ants crawling around all over their hill, but he could see a number of dry leaves that had fallen there, and these were trembling, vibrating, and jiggling back and forth. Not knowing what was actually going on, he assumed the leaves were alive. But they moved only because they were kept in motion by the ever-busy ants.

The Brownian movement proved that water molecules are in constant motion. In liquids, atoms and molecules dance around, sliding over each other without ever stopping. Molecules of which solid things are made don't slide, but they vibrate and swing around their fixed places like the coils of a spring mattress when jostled. If you could look at your table with an atomic eye, so to speak, you would recognize it as a complex network of vibrating atoms and molecules.

The atoms and molecules of a gas are likewise in constant motion. About one hundred years ago scientists were greatly interested in this concept because atomic motion presented a chance to explain the famous gas laws—the well-known laws that describe how trapped gases behave. Any law of Nature is always a great challenge, because it demands an explanation. And it turned out that atomic and molecular motion was the only correct explanation for the orderly behavior of the gases. The train of thought followed by scientists of the second half of the century was as follows:

Gases consist of atoms and molecules that are constantly in free flight, dashing back and forth in all directions like a swarm of little flies. Flies, however, usually zip around in mad circles and rarely ever collide. Not so the molecules of a gas. These dash along in straight lines until they hit other molecules that happen to cross their course. Two colliding molecules rebound like two cue balls, and each dashes off in another direction. Everyone of the molecules in a gas is constantly on the move, repeatedly colliding with many others in the game. So each molecule follows a mad zig-zag course.

The molecules in a gas also keep hitting the

walls of the container which encloses the gas. When they hit, they rebound and return to the everlasting free-for-all within the gas mass. There are so many molecules hitting the walls so many times in every second that these millions and millions of little pushes amount to a constant pressure against the walls.

If a gas is compressed, all the molecules are forced into a smaller space. Then their chances of colliding with each other are greatly increased. Each molecule collides more often with its partners, and the walls, too, get a much stronger pounding. In other words, the pressure of the gas against the walls is increased when the gas is squeezed into a smaller volume.

Now this is a proposition that will delight any physicist, particularly if he has a knack for mathematics! There are so many cubic inches of space filled with so much gas; there is a pressure of so many pounds per square inch; and the molecules can be assumed to fly around with a speed of so many feet per second. With this kind of information a student of mathematical physics can sit down and calculate how often a molecule collides with another one in each second, and how far it would travel on the average between collisions. And he can discover through calculation whether a mass of flying molecules would behave like a real gas.

Mathematics was already well developed in

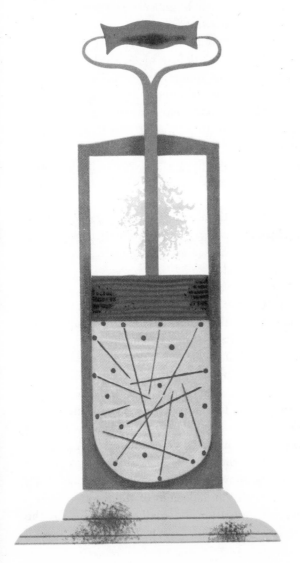

the nineteenth century. Newton had calculated the motions of the planets; calculus had long been in use, and mathematicians knew how to handle the tricky differential equations. These methods of higher mathematics are powerful tools of theory, and they were applied to calculating the motions of molecules in a gas.

The calculations turned out to be remarkably successful. They showed that a great mass of atoms and molecules buzzing around would indeed behave according to laws that are valid for a gas. This so-called "kinetic theory of gases" worked so well as to become final proof of the constant motion of atoms and molecules. It was also the final proof that matter really consists of atoms, even though nobody had ever seen an atom with his own two eyes.

When the motion of atoms was recognized, it spelled the final defeat of Aristotle's brand of science. For one thing, it explained the nature of heat. Until almost a hundred years ago scientists believed that a body was hot because it contained heat. This was an argument true to the form of Aristotle: heat was a kind of substance that filled hot bodies. Even the great Lavoisier listed heat as one of the chemical elements in his table. Today we know that heat is motion of atoms and molecules. If a flatiron is heated, its atoms start moving faster. When we touch it, the stronger pounding of its atoms against the skin gives us the sensation of heat.

Even an ice cube contains a small amount of heat. If it could be magnified a hundred million times, we would recognize it as a huge superstructure built like a three-dimensional lattice work of single H_2O molecules. They move constantly. But they do so by vibrating slowly and sluggishly. This is why an ice cube is cold to the touch.

In a flame the motion of atoms and molecules is extremely violent. They dash around with great speed—and this is why a flame is hot. A glass jar taken from the shelf is normal to the touch. Its molecules move much more slowly, but not quite so slowly as the molecules of the ice cubes. So a body's temperature is actually determined by the degree of molecular movement. But what happens if we put the ice cube in the jar and place both over the fire?

When the fast-moving molecules in the flame bounce against the molecules of the glass, the latter too, start moving faster. In turn, the glass molecules bounce against the ice molecules and start them vibrating faster, too. It's like a pool game with the balls bouncing against each other.

As more and more heat is supplied to the ice, its molecules are moving faster and faster. Finally, the ice molecules are vibrating so fast that they break loose from each other. They begin to roll around freely, forming a dense pack of ever-moving molecules: the ice has melted and has become water. The heating goes on, causing the water molecules to move ever faster. Presently a few of them are kicked above the water surface and escape into the free air. As the water is brought to boil by constant heating, the molecules will escape in great numbers: they are expelled from the water as steam. In hot steam the molecules are dashing around with their greatest force —enough force to push the lid off the jar.

We know the tremendous power in steam. When a mass of furious steam molecules are released against a piston, they push it along with great force—enough to drive a locomotive that draws a hundred cars. And so it was the power of countless moving atoms and molecules that began to drive the machines of man in the technical age. It was the power of steam that drove his engines and ships, and turned the generators that brought him from the gaslight era into the age of electricity.

Steam was a mighty servant—an almost magic servant. But it was not yet the mighty Genie of our story that dwells in the atom. Steam was a hungry servant that had to be fed constantly. It drew its power from fire, and it became necessary to keep countless fires burning all the time. The fires of the technical age cut deep into our precious resources of coal and oil.

By 1890 man was feeling pretty smug about his accomplishments in science and engineering. He thought that he had the forces of Nature at his command. He knew of the atom. He knew of its size, and he knew how much the different kinds of atoms weigh. He knew of their tremendous number, and of the great power that lay in their furious motion. But he didn't know what the atom really was. He still thought it was an indestructible and indivisible thing—just as its name implied.

What a surprise was in the offing!

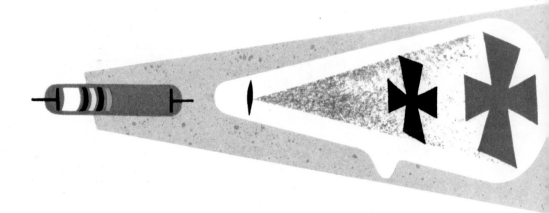

Early experimenters discovered that electrons would flow through a tube pumped free of air. From tubes such as these came the television picture tube of today.

Metals Alive!

By 1890 man had not only harnessed the power of steam; he was also well on the road to making electricity his servant in all civilized nations. As it was with the power of steam, the invisible power of electricity was first used by man without real understanding of its nature.

More than a hundred years ago physicists first suspected that electricity, like matter itself, is made of atoms. They thought that atoms of electricity are identical tiny bits; that all have the same tiny charge of negative electricity. If a large number of these little charge carriers are deposited on a body, it is said to be electrically charged. As early as 1874 the English physicist Stoney even invented a name for these atoms of electricity; he called them "electrons."

Like the atom, the electron had a name before it was discovered. And as with the atom, the discovery of the electron was only a question of time, because it really did and does exist.

When scientists make a new discovery, news reporters like to say that they found something new in their "test tubes." The electron was really discovered in a tube. But it wasn't the kind of tube chemists use; it was a tube that many generations later developed into such noble great-grandchildren as the radio tube and the television

tube. These latest descendants, too, bear the family name. They are still called "electron tubes," even though the bulbous eye of the TV-tube certainly looks nothing like a piece of pipe.

The ancestor of our modern electron tubes was really a tube; it was a piece of glass pipe closed at both ends. Metal wires were sealed into each end of the glass and a voltage put on these wires. At first nothing happened, just as nothing happens to the voltage that lies across the metal contacts of every wall plug in your living room. The voltage cannot discharge because the air between the contacts is a good insulator. But, knowing that in the tube the voltage is well insulated by the air between the wires, physicists pumped the air out of the tube to see what would happen. This removed more and more of the insulator between the wires, and as the air became thinner and thinner, something began to happen. A silent discharge took place: streamers of soft light stretched from one wire to the other, producing a strange, wavering glow of red and purplish colors. As more and more air was pumped out, the glow grew weaker and finally vanished. However, opposite the negative wire—which was called the "cathode"—the glass walls of the tube glowed with a flickering light of a pale green color. It was a kind of fluorescent light like the eerie glow of rotting wood in the night.

The German physicists Hittorf and Schuster and the English scientist Sir William Crookes were foremost among the researchers in this fascinating field of discharge tubes. Soon they discovered that the glow was caused by a kind of radiation that was given off by the cathode wire. The rays traveled across the empty tube, and when they hit the opposite wall they caused the glass to shine with that eerie glow. Little objects put in their path inside the tube—a little cross, for example—cast a shadow on the tube walls.

Later it was found that the rays could be deflected by a magnet held close to the tube. This could only mean that the rays were not ordinary light rays; they had to be a stream of tiny charged particles that emerged from the negative wire. This meant further that they had to bear a negative charge. Crookes first called these particle rays "radiant matter," but soon they were called by the name Stoney had already chosen: electrons!

The year was 1895. In his laboratory at the University of Würzburg, Germany, Wilhelm Konrad Roentgen was making experiments with the fluorescent light produced by electron rays. He built himself a so-called fluorescent screen—a piece of cardboard painted with certain highly fluorescent chemicals. It was the forerunner of our modern television and radar screens, which also light up when electrons strike their surface. One day this screen was placed a few feet away from an electron tube which Roentgen was operating at a rather high voltage. Suddenly Roentgen discovered that the screen glowed in the dark even though the captive electron rays in his tube couldn't possibly reach over to the screen. He took a blank piece of cardboard and placed it between the tube and the screen. The screen still glowed. Excited, he ran to the workshop and selected a thin piece of sheet metal and placed it between the tube and the screen. The glow was weakened, but it was still there.

Roentgen drew his conclusions fast. The tube must be the source of a new kind of rays that penetrated cardboard and sheet metal as though they were made of glass.

Next, he placed his outstretched palm between the tube and the screen. What he saw gave him quite a start. On the screen there was visible the skeleton hand of a ghost. He could see the thin, spidery bones of the fingers. He moved his hand. The bony hand moved, too, as though it were a

1895

ghostly mirror image. Roentgen was seeing the bones of his own living hand!

The rays from the tube penetrated both flesh and bone of the living body. Because the bones are somewhat heavier and denser than the soft tissue of the flesh, they cast a shadow. Roentgen knew he had discovered a strange kind of rays unknown before. Because he didn't know what they were, he called them "X-rays"; but in German-speaking countries they were soon called "Roentgen-rays."

His discovery was a sensation, and Roentgen found himself famous over-night. Medical doctors recognized at once that X-rays permitted them to look inside the human body without cutting it open. They could watch broken bones and body organs in action. To this day X-rays remain the most important tool in the diagnosis of human

disorders. They turned out to be of tremendous benefit to suffering mankind.

It took scientists almost a decade to explore the true nature of X-rays. Somehow the electrons dashing through the tube must be responsible for them. Presently it was found that X-rays grew much stronger when the electrons were hurled against a solid block of metal. Brought to a sudden, dead stop in the metal, the electrons gave off the X-rays. What happens when electrical charges are jarred is that they produce radiation akin to light—so-called electromagnetic radiation. In the Roentgen tube the fast beam of electrons suffer a tremendous jar when they ram against the metal block. It is such jars that produce the highly energetic electromagnetic rays we know as penetrating X-rays.

Electron tubes and how they led to the discov-

44

ery of X-rays may appear to be out of place in a book that is supposed to tell the story of the atom. Both the electron tube and the X-rays were explored by scientists who actually had not made the atom the prime object of their study. But the road of science is tortuous. Frequently the men traveling it do not know where it will lead them.

Without the electron tube there wouldn't have been any X-rays. Without the X-rays there wouldn't have been any studies by scientists trying to find out what the X-rays are. Among these studies there was one, in fact, that led into a dead-end street. This particular study did not yield the explanation of X-rays, even though this was the aim. The investigating scientist could not find the correct explanation, because he had made a wrong assumption. And but for this error we might still think of the atom as a little hard, indestuctible ball!

The year after the discovery of X-rays, Henri Becquerel of France became interested in a cheap metal called uranium. In a dictionary compiled at that time uranium was defined as "a heavy, practically worthless metal." Little did Becquerel know that this worthless metal was to be the star of important scientific events—then, and again fifty years later. It interested him because it was known to make materials fluorescent when added to them to form "uranium salts." He thought that X-rays were somehow related to the eerie glow that electrons or sunlight produced in fluorescent materials. Uranium salts were known to give off strong fluorescent light for a while after they had been exposed to sunlight.

So Becquerel ran a series of experiments in which he first put samples of uranium salts in the sun. Then he took the softly glowing samples and placed them on top of photographic plates tightly wrapped in black paper. When he developed his plates, he found that the uranium salts had indeed exposed them. The plates showed foggy spots at all those places where the samples had been put. The salts had exposed the plates right through the thick wrappers, just as though they had been the source of penetrating X-rays. Becquerel thought he had something.

One day it started to rain in Paris, and it didn't stop raining for a whole week. There was no sunshine in which Becquerel could expose his samples of uranium salts. He stopped his experiments, but after three days without sunshine he got impatient. He went ahead with his experiments—without sunshine. He placed another sample of uranium salt on his wrapped photographic plates even though this sample had not been in the sun and did not show the fluorescent glow. The sample exposed the plates, anyway! The penetrating rays from the uranium salt had nothing to do with sunshine or the fluorescent light. They had nothing to do with the fact that uranium salt was used, not pure uranium metal.

Uranium, then, was constantly "alive"—giving off a strange new kind of radiation that fogged photographic plates right through their protective wrappers. It was radioactive. Becquerel had discovered a new phenomenon. To us, in the atomic age, "radioactivity" sounds familiar. Its discovery was the beginning of something entirely new.

Tell-Tale Rays

RADIOACTIVITY was such a new, unheard-of thing that scientists were baffled. But uranium was only the beginning. If scientists thought uranium was hard to explain, they didn't know that their problem was soon to become more than two million times bigger.

When scientists run into a roadblock such as this, they go after more facts, often searching blindly. Among the scientists who responded to this challenge were a married couple in Paris—Pierre and Marie Curie. He was a physicist, she primarily a chemist.

Their first step was to go back to the very source of radioactivity: not to uranium itself but to raw uranium ore as it is found in the earth's crust, mixed with other metals and minerals.

For some time the Curies tested the strength of radioactivity of a great number of uranium ore samples. Some samples were found more radioactive than pure uranium. But uranium was only part of the mineral mixtures they were using, other materials forming the bulk. There was only one conclusion: among these materials must exist a substance more radioactive than uranium itself.

Madame Curie went to work separating the uranium ore into its many component parts. It was a chemist's work on a grand scale. Normally chemists keep their samples in handy bottles that contain only a few ounces of chemicals. Madame Curie started out with a whole ton of uranium ore. For months their wooden building in Paris looked more like a factory than a laboratory.

Slowly her ton of ore shrank as she threw out the dead minerals and the uranium itself. With every step in the long process of elimination, her sample grew smaller, and the strength of its radioactivity increased. In time she discovered a new element that was highly radioactive. She named this second, rarer radioactive element "polonium," after Poland, her native country.

But there was still a small remainder, free of uranium and polonium, yet still radiating. It must contain still another radioactive material. So Madame Curie forged ahead. Presently she had whittled down her original ton to a tiny sample weighing less than 1/100 of an ounce. And this tiny sample was more than 2 million

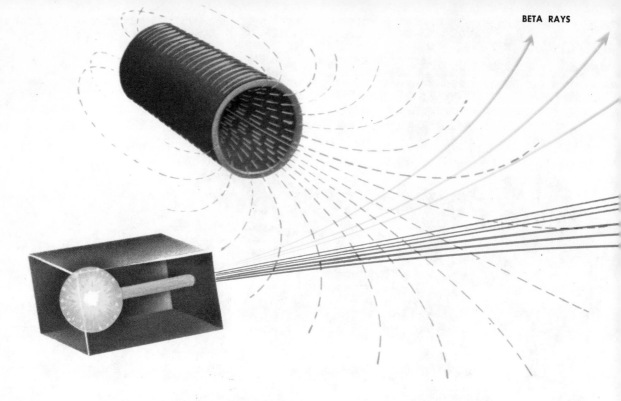

times more radioactive than the same weight of pure uranium! It radiated so strongly that it glowed faintly in the dark. And this sample was always a few degrees warmer than the temperature of the laboratory—it kept itself warm all the time.

This amazing sample of matter, too, turned out to be a new element. Madame Curie called it "the radiating one"—radium.

Uranium, polonium—radium! The chance discovery of Henri Becquerel and the patient work of Madame Curie now shook the firm foundation of physics. Up to now physicists had been dealing with forces of mechanics, with vibrations of sound, with heat, electricity, magnetism, and light. Everything, or almost everything, had been well understood and, together with the tiny atom, had found its place in the orderly files of physics. Now appeared this enigmatic trio—uranium, polonium, and radium. Rays and radiation became the talk of the day. What was it that emerged from the unseen depths of the atoms of which these strange metals were made?

It was several years before scientists found out about the nature of these rays that fogged photographic plates, electrified air, and—turned out to be vicious and dangerous to man! These rays

slowly caused painful and dangerous burns in people who unduly exposed themselves to them. But in this battle for knowledge man was not without weapons. Studies of electron tubes had provided some experience with rays.

An ordinary magnet placed near an electron tube was known to bend the streams of electrons to a curve, while without the magnet they travel in a straight beam. This behavior of the electrons was well understood. A moving electrical charge had long been known to act like a magnet. This is the basis of the everyday electromagnet used in switches and relays and in the ordinary doorbell. When an electric current is run through a coiled wire, a magnetic field is created like that of an ordinary magnet. Similarly, a moving magnet produces an electric field. This close kinship between electricity and magnetism was discovered more than a hundred years ago and led to a field of physics and engineering called "electromagnetism."

Now, the laws of electromagnetism explained why the fast-moving beam of electrons in the tube would run in a curve when a magnet was held near the tube. The electrons—little carriers of negative electricity that they are—react to the field of the magnet and are drawn to the side.

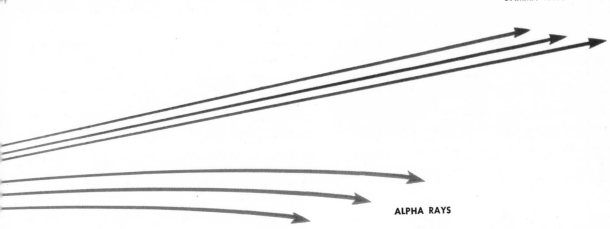

ALPHA RAYS

Knowing all this, scientists went after radium with a magnet. But the test wasn't as simple as with the electron tube, in which the electrons run in beams. The rays emerging from a sample of radium fly off in all directions like rays from a miniature sun. So the first task was to produce a linear beam of radium rays. This was done by placing the radium sample in a hollow piece of lead, which is able to absorb radium rays. The hollow block of lead had a small hole through which the rays from the radium inside emerged in a thin straight beam.

Then a magnet was placed near the hole so that the rays shot through its magnetic field: It was found that some rays from the radium did indeed bend to the side. This proved that the rays consisted of streams of charged particles.

One kind of rays bent to the right. They were called "alpha-rays," after the first letter of the Greek alphabet. Another kind of rays bent to the left. They were called "beta-rays," after the second letter of the Greek alphabet. The beta-rays carried a negative charge—a fact that was obvious because the position of the magnet was such that negative charges would bend to the left side. The beta-rays turned out to be well known—they were streams of electrons. But these beta-electrons from radium were much faster than the ordinary electrons physicists had first discovered in their electron tubes. Radium shot off its electrons at a speed almost as great as that of light, which is over 186,000 miles a second!

The alpha-rays were much harder to identify.

They had to be carriers of a positive charge, because the magnet bent them to the right—opposite to the bending of the beta-rays. But beyond this, the researchers were baffled; they didn't find at first any known particle that would behave this way.

Then a third variety of rays was found in radium radiation. They were logically called "gamma-rays," because gamma is the third letter of the Greek alphabet. These rays went straight through the field of the magnet without bending. Light and X-rays do the same. Gamma-rays were, indeed, found to be a particularly powerful and penetrating kind of X-rays.

The battle for knowledge went on. Next the fire was concentrated on the particles that made up alpha-rays. Shrewd experiments were set up that put the alpha-particle on the witness stand. With their experiments scientists kept asking questions brilliant in their logic. Finally, during the first years of this century, the alpha-particle broke down under this relentless cross-examination. It surrendered its secrets, above all its personal description; weight: four times heavier than a hydrogen atom; electrical charge: positive with two charge units, each the size of the electron's charge.

The electron, incidentally, was a co-defendant in this trial. Its weight was revealed to be extremely small: almost 2,000 times lighter than a hydrogen atom, the lightest atom known in Nature. When it comes to weight, the electron is a sheer nothing compared to the tiny atom itself.

49

The famous English physicist Sir Ernest Rutherford and his chemical co-worker, Frederick Soddy, did most of this fascinating detective work. In the United States, Dr. Robert A. Millikan concentrated his efforts on the electron. He measured its charge in known electrical units and could then compute its unbelievably small weight.

In 1903, Rutherford and Soddy came forth with their explanation of radioactivity. It destroyed the atom of Dalton, and the element of Boyle. It proved that the atom had been misnamed since Democritus first named it. No longer could it be considered "uncuttable." Rutherford and Soddy showed that some atoms, at least, cut themselves to pieces by their own actions.

An alpha-ray is the birth cry of a new atom! Not all atoms are created eternally. New ones are created all the time.

A radium atom weighs 226 times more than a hydrogen atom; its atomic weight is 226. An alpha-particle weighs 4 times more than a hydrogen atom. So when a radium atom shoots off an alpha-particle, it loses 4 weight units in the process, and it winds up with an atomic weight of 222. That makes it a different atom. Atoms weighing 222 units are atoms of a different chemical element. Their name is "radon"—rare, heavy gas.

By giving off an alpha-particle, then, the radium atom transforms itself into an atom of a different kind. A new element is created. Boyle was wrong, at least in this case: for elements *can* be created from different ones. Dalton was wrong, too; for one kind of atom *can* change into another kind.

Radon also is a radioactive element. Its atoms, too, break apart and transform into atoms of still another element. Finally, by the process of successive breakdowns, the original radium atom is transformed into an atom of the metal lead. Lead atoms are stable. They remain forever as they finally emerge at the end of this so-called "radioactive decay series."

If a beta-ray is expelled from a radioactive atom, the atom doesn't lose any weight to speak of, because electrons are so extremely light. But it was found that the removal of a beta-ray with its negative charge does result in a transmutation of an atom into another one. The omission of a gamma ray, however, does not change the atom's chemical nature.

But what happens to alpha-particles, the fragments shot out of radioactive atoms? Alpha-particles have a weight of 4 atomic units. There is an element whose atoms have an atomic weight of 4. Its name is helium—the light gas used to float balloons and blimps. When Rutherford and Soddy held a sample of the radioactive gas radon inside a sealed bottle, they found indeed a very small amount of helium. Radon atoms had transformed themselves into atoms of helium and atoms of yet another element akin to polonium!

Each radioactive atom can break up only a single time in all its life. Then it becomes another kind of atom. The new one may also be radioactive, like radon, or it may be stable, like helium. Thus a radioactive atom "decays," or breaks down by stages, until it becomes an atom of inert lead.

In a sample of radium there is such a tremendous number of atoms that some are breaking apart all the time. Their fragments are shooting out of the sample constantly.

Physicists know exactly what percentage of their radioactive atoms will break up during the next year. They know that 1,580 years from now exactly one half of the atoms in a sample of radium will have broken down. This span of time is the "half-life" of radium; after that time exactly one half of the original radium still is "alive." Another 1,580 years later only one fourth of the original radium atoms will still be present. Uranium, on the other hand, has a half-life of over 4 billion years. Other radioactive elements have half-lives of only minutes or even seconds.

An element with a short half-life is a much stronger radiator than one with a long half-life. In an element with a short half-life the atoms are breaking up so fast that many break-ups occur in a single second. A long-lived element loses its atoms slowly—a few at a time. This is why the short-lived radium is more than 2 million times more radioactive than the sluggish, long-lived uranium.

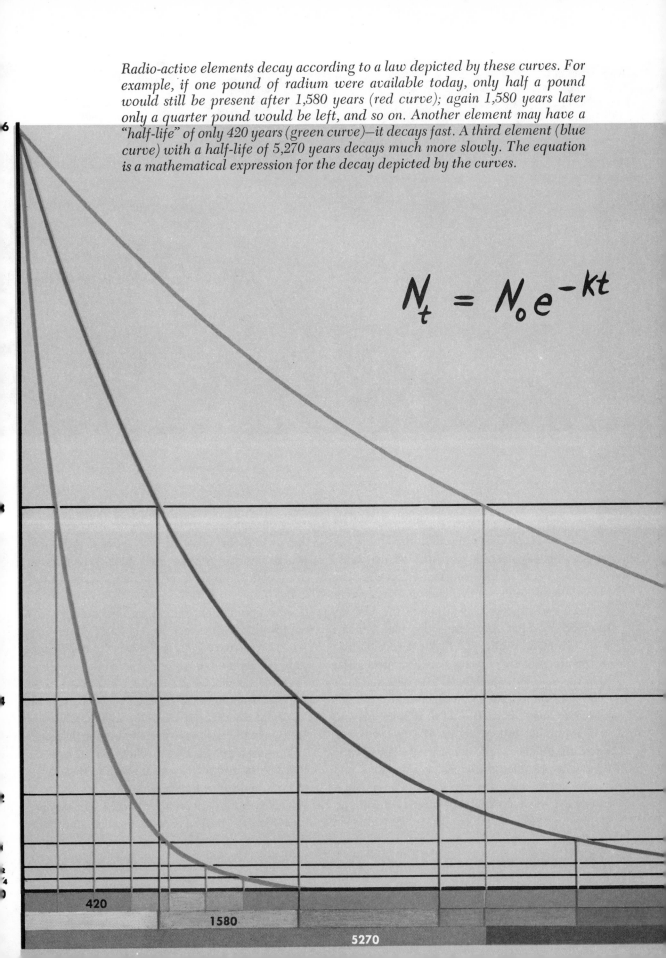

Radio-active elements decay according to a law depicted by these curves. For example, if one pound of radium were available today, only half a pound would still be present after 1,580 years (red curve); again 1,580 years later only a quarter pound would be left, and so on. Another element may have a "half-life" of only 420 years (green curve)—it decays fast. A third element (blue curve) with a half-life of 5,270 years decays much more slowly. The equation is a mathematical expression for the decay depicted by the curves.

$$N_t = N_0 e^{-kt}$$

420

1580

5270

E=mc²

AFTER Madame Curie discovered radium, scientists were fascinated most by the strange radiation that poured fourth constantly from the unknown depths of its atoms. These rays, of course, were the most spectacular aspect of the radioactive elements. But the Curies also found that a piece of radium is always a little warmer than its surroundings. This property was less spectacular than the flashing rays, but no less remarkable.

Radium turned out to be a constant and mysterious source of heat. If a bit of radium was put into a thimble full of water, the water would warm up. If the thimble was perfectly insulated to prevent loss of heat, the water became hotter and finally would start to boil. The radium could keep such water boiling slowly for centuries. So in any tiny piece of radium there lies hidden a tremendous amount of energy that trickles out slowly.

Even before the turn of the century, therefore, the discovery of radioactivity gave science the very first inkling of atomic energy. But for a number of years nobody had even the slightest hunch where this energy came from. Radioactive energy was against all laws of science known at that time.

The first understanding of this mystery was achieved by the great Albert Einstein in 1905 when he discovered a new law of Nature. He was only twenty-six years old when, for the first time, he wrote down what was to become the most famous equation in science. This was part of his theory of relativity. It read: $E=mc^2$. E stands for energy, m for mass or matter, and c^2 for the speed of light multiplied by itself. The equal sign means that energy and matter are the same thing, if the latter is multiplied by the quantity c^2.

This is a cold scientific statement, but its deep meaning can be understood through our fable. The fisherman, too, had discovered that a mighty force was contained in a tiny vessel. . . .

The clue to the Einstein formula lies in the quantity c^2. The speed of light is 186,000 miles per second. This great number multiplied by itself becomes 34,596,000,000. According to Einstein's equation, a mass must be multiplied by this number to find the energy that would be equivalent to this mass. It isn't necessary to tell in what units the energy would be expressed: the result is big in any units!

The Einstein equation only tells that matter and energy are the same thing in two different shapes. The equation itself doesn't tell in what way matter could actually be converted into energy. But the formula gave scientists the assurance that there could be such a thing as a virtually endless source of energy like radium. So, from 1905 on, scientists had a formula—without instructions.

Nature herself has the instructions, and she has made use of them since the beginning of time. Today we know that atomic energy powers the universe and fires the lights in the sky. Our own sun, for example, delivers energy in the form of sunshine. In every second 4 million tons of its mass are converted into pure energy and poured into space, and this has been going on for billions of years. The millions of other stars pour out energy in like amounts. Nature, in fact, is wasteful of energy beyond comprehension.

The source of stellar energy could not possibly lie in any known chemical fuels. If the sun's energy were produced by the combustion of high-grade coal and pure oxygen, it would burn to a dead heap of ashes within a few thousand years. Like all other stars the sun shines by an atomic fire. Deep in the core of the sun, energy is broiled out of matter in fearful quantities. Slowly this energy trickles through the gaseous body of the sun and flows outward from its surface as sunshine.

A tiny portion of the sun's energy falls upon the earth and keeps us alive. All our energy resources—coal, oil, and water power—go back to the sun for their beginnings, back to the atomic

fire raging deep behind the sun's gas walls. Plants that lived thousands and millions of years ago thrived in the shine of the same sun that warms us today. These plants died and were buried under many layers of earth and rock, and under this pressure were slowly transformed to peat and coal. Now we dig these up and use them for fuel. Our oil, too, comes from organisms that were once alive thanks to sunshine. Even today the sun provides us with power. Its heat evaporates ocean water and sends it across the continents to fall as rain. The rain fills the lakes behind our dams, and through broad pipes the water is directed against the blades of huge water turbines that drive generators to produce electric power for our cities, towns, and factories. It is from the atomic fire deep in the core of the sun that our civilization gets all its power.

Such was the reasoning of scientists in the decades after Einstein first published his equation in 1905. However, in the beginning their reasoning could not go far beyond the recognition that there is such a thing as atomic energy. Very few scientists, if any, speculated about its practical use in the future. Too little was known about the atom at that time. Even the term "atomic energy" —so familiar to us now—was not used. A few specialists spoke of "sub-atomic" energy; they used this term to indicate that the energy of radioactive elements has its origin somewhere inside the atom.

The interior of the atom—this was the great challenge of science during the first decade of this century.

Radio-activity—atoms breaking apart! It was a great shock to all scientists. No longer could the atom be considered an indestructible, indivisible, hard ball. There were the alpha- and beta-rays: positive and negative fragments that emerged from the unknown depths of the atom's interior. As these fragments proved, the atom must consist of still smaller parts electrically charged.

The shock of the discovery of these phenomena was quickly replaced by the excitement and promise of the next big question:

What is the architecture of the atom?

The Atomic
Shooting Range

Sᴜᴘᴘᴏsᴇ that atoms could be put on a string like so many pearls. A girl begins to string herself an atomic necklace 25 inches long. She is very skillful and has great endurance: she strings at the rate of one atom per second, and never stops day or night.

When will she finish her necklace?

Not before 200 years are up!

This is only another way of expressing how small atoms are. At this point of our story we must try to visualize the extreme smallness of atoms. Although this is virtually impossible, we must make the attempt because our next step will lead us into the interior of the atom.

The thought of such a step is fantastic. Here is the atom, much too small to be seen and grasped. Any ordinary method of study is doomed to failure. But in the beginning of our century science faced the problem of probing this tiny structure and tracing its architecture. Fortunately, a meth-

Rutherford's atomic shooting range

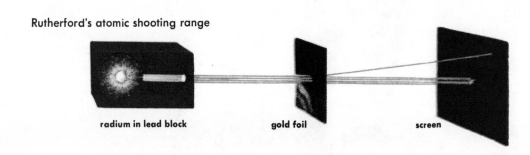

radium in lead block   gold foil   screen

od was known for tracing single atoms. It is a simple method, and not only does it trace a single atom; it even traces the tiny fragments that emerge from the inside of radioactive atoms. It's the tremendous speed of the particles of radioactive rays that makes their traces visible.

The method makes use of fluorescent screens of the type already encountered in our chapter on electron rays and X-rays. Take a single alpha-particle that dashes away from an atom of radium as the result of an atomic break-up. It has a speed of many thousands of miles per second. It crashes into a fluorescent screen with a terrific impact. The alpha-particle is a very tiny fragment of an atom, mind you—but it has a lot of wham owing to its tremendous speed. When it slams into the fluorescent screen, it causes a tiny explosion which can be seen under a microscope as a sudden minute flash.

You can demonstrate this action with the self-luminous dial of your wristwatch. The self-luminous coating on the dial is a mixture of radioactive material and fluorescent paint. In every second hundreds of alpha-particles slam into the

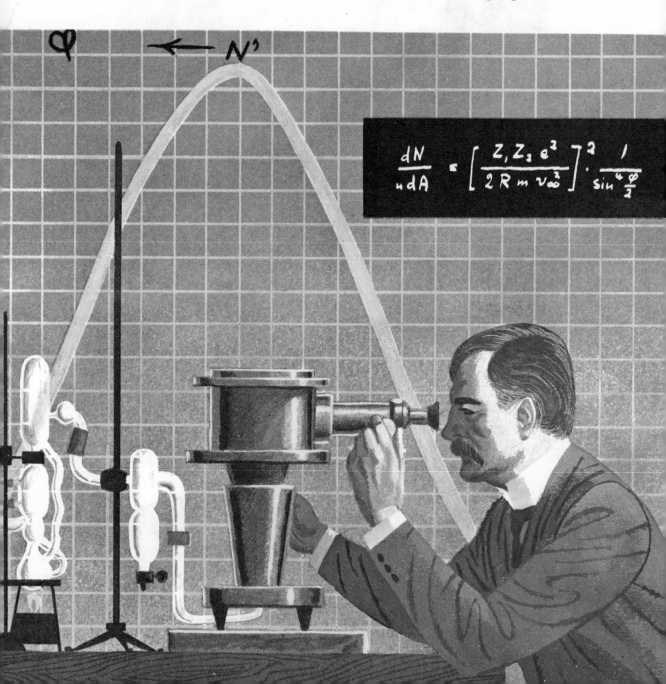

$$\frac{dN}{ndA} = \left[\frac{Z_1 Z_2 e^2}{2 R m v_\infty^2}\right]^2 \cdot \frac{1}{\sin^4 \frac{\theta}{2}}$$

fluorescent paint. Each one of them makes a tiny flash, and the constant sparkling makes the dial glow dimly in the dark. Under a microscope the dial looks like a display of miniature fireworks. The flashes produced by atomic particles in fluorescent materials are called "scintillations."

The fact that a single alpha-particle could be traced was very exciting to scientists. It meant that this particle could be used as a tool of exploration. As always in science, when a new thing is discovered it becomes a tool for discovering other things that lie around the next corner. The development of the rocket, for example, enabled man to send hundreds of miles into the upper atmosphere mechanical messengers which faithfully report back to earth what they see, hear, and feel. Likewise, early in our century scientists could shoot their alpha-particle into the atom. It was small enough to serve as a messenger, because it was known to be a fragment of the atom. To explore the atom, then, scientists used atomic bullets.

The first scientists to do so were the two German physicists Geiger and Marsden. They observed some very strange things, and their results encouraged Sir Ernest Rutherford to persue this line of research more closely. Rutherford was the famous English scientist who had been able to explain the nature of radioactivity. He had shown that atoms break up, and through his work he had posed the question as to what the atom's architecture is. Now he began a long series of shooting experiments, for which he built himself an atomic shooting range.

His atomic machine gun was a sample of radium buried inside a block of lead with an opening for the rays to escape. This block he placed inside a glass jar that was pumped out to a good vacuum, because he did not want any interference with his bullets by air molecules. His atomic bullets traveled in a straight line, like bullets from a machine gun fired at close range.

To make the impacts of his bullets visible he used a flourescent screen attached to the front of a microscope. First he placed the microscope behind the screen so that his line of sight through

the microscope was directly into the m... his "gun." On the screen he saw a constan... ling at the point where the bullets from t... were striking.

Then he mounted in front of the gun a... tremely thin piece of gold foil—less than a h... dred thousandth of an inch thick. Thin it w... but atoms are very small. For the atoms, the go... foil represented a thick wall, more than 2,00... atoms deep. And each gold atom weighed as... much as 197 hydrogen atoms—the atoms of gold being among the heaviest there are. Atomically speaking, therefore, this wall of gold represented solid armor.

Again Rutherford peered through his microscope. To his amazement he saw the constant sparkling on the screen as before. It was as though his gun were shooting through a ghost: the alpha-particles were still bombarding the screen. They were pouring through the wall of atoms represented by the foil as though it were not there at all!

The wall was thick. If the gold atoms had been as big as baseballs, the wall would have been about 400 feet thick—more than a whole city block thick. And the atomic bullets went right through this kind of wall. They tore into the screen just as they did before the gold foil was put in their path. The target spot on the screen still flickered and sparkled as bright as before.

Right then and there, an age-old idea of the atom vanished into nothingness. Atoms could not be solid—they could not be the impenetrable, absolutely hard little balls they were thought to be.

Rutherford kept spying through his microscope, the gold foil still in place. Then he saw something. There was a tiny flash on the screen— far out to the side of the target area. Then he saw another flash, this time to the other side, right out at the rim of his field of view. . . . Then another one at still another place.

He shifted his microscope to the side, so his line of sight was no longer into the muzzle of the gun. The screen was now dark. But there—there was a tiny flash, where just a single bullet had struck!

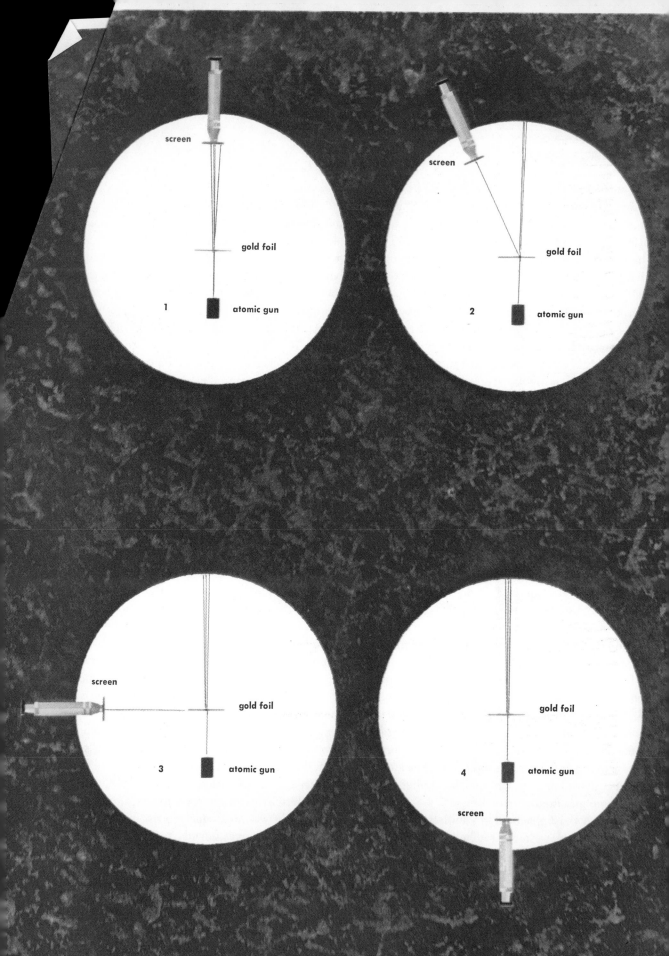

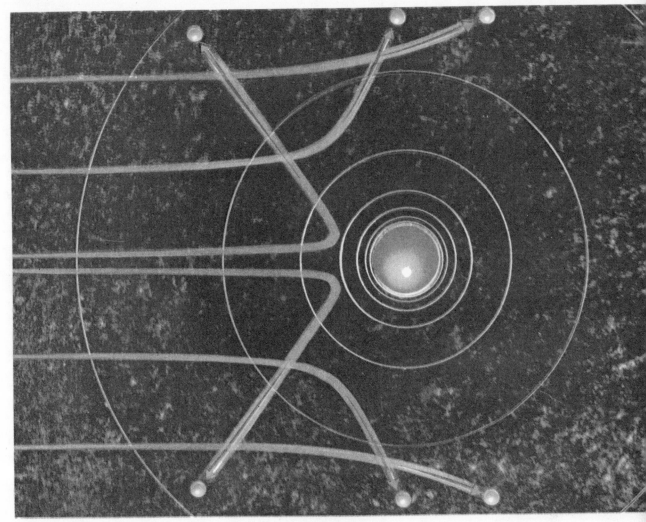

The closer the alpha-particles get to the nucleus, the more sharply they are deflected.

He brought the microscope and screen around to a position at right angles to the gold foil.

His line of sight was now directly across the beam of bullets. Again a single flash on the screen! This bullet must have bounced off something; it had reached the screen by ricocheting at a right angle.

Next he moved the microscope and screen behind the "gun." His line of sight was now in the direction of his bullets, like that of a machine gunner behind his weapon. Another flash on the screen: this single bullet must have bounced right back at him like a bullet from armor plate!

Rutherford repeated his experiments many times. He counted the bullets that went straight through his wall of atoms and he counted those that bounced off in the various directions. The result was amazing. Only one out of more than 8,000 bullets bounced!

Imagine a huge stack of thousands of tissue paper boxes each containing a single small marble. When you spray this stack with birdshot, almost all of them tear right through the whole stack. Only a few will happen to strike a marble, glance off, or rebound. If the marbles are small enough, chances are that only one out of 8,000 bullets will ricochet.

That was approximately the situation encountered by Lord Rutherford. He reasoned that the heavy wall of gold atoms was actually nothing more than a stack of almost empty shells. But something *must* be inside each shell—a small center, a hard core which caused the rare ricochets. This core must be unbelievably small—much smaller than the atom itself. The core had to be very small because the chance of hitting it was so small.

Rutherford called this little core the "nucleus" of the atom. From his record of hits and misses he learned how small the nucleus is in relation to the atom: ten to fifty thousand times smaller!

The atom is indeed an empty shell—almost empty, that is. Practically the entire weight of the atom is concentrated in the tiny nucleus. The rest is empty space.

These are not the only findings that Rutherford's tiny messengers brought back from the interior of the atom. The nucleus not only is extremely tiny and fabulously heavy for its size; it is also electrically charged. This was proved by the way in which the alpha-particles bounced off the atomic nuclei.

Previously we noted that the alpha-particle bears two units of positive electrical charge. The nucleus, too, is positively charged. The nuclei of gold atoms each bear a very strong electrical charge—79 units! Now, there is a force acting between two like electrical charges, a strong force that pushes them apart. Conversely, a positive and a negative charge attract each other as a magnet attracts a piece of iron. Since the alpha-particle and any nucleus are both positively charged, they repel each other. As the alpha-bullet approaches the target nucleus, the force acting to keep them apart becomes greater and greater. As with a tiny, invisible hand, the nucleus pushes the alpha-particle to the side so that it continues its flight in a different direction. If the alpha-bullet approaches the nucleus almost dead-center, it is pushed back at a steep angle. In the case of a rare shot directly at the center of the nucleus, the alpha-particle is slowed down, comes to a stop a short distance from the nucleus, and—repelled by a tremendous force—is hurled back.

Thus Sir Ernest Rutherford did well with his experiments on the atomic shooting range. He discovered the nucleus of the atom, measured its unbelievably small size, and proved that it is electrically charged.

The atomic nucleus was the tiny vessel in which the Genie of our story lay imprisoned. The year of its discovery was 1911.

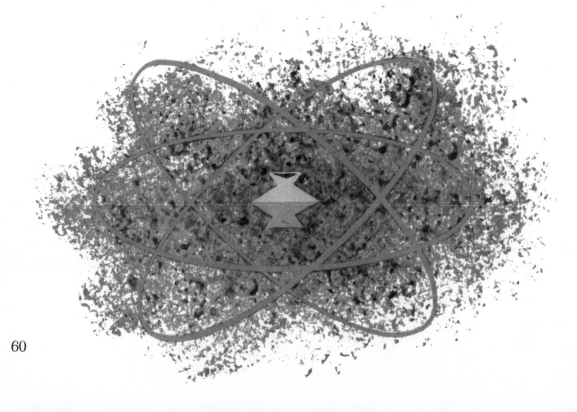

Why Is The Atom So Big?

For a long time scientists had been baffled by the smallness of the atom. After the discovery of the tiny nucleus, the problem reversed itself completely. If the nucleus were enlarged to the size of a small glass marble, the whole atom would be as big as a giant balloon measuring more than 300 feet across! Scientists were hard

put to explain why the atom is so big. Its architecture, that is to say, was still a mystery.

Rutherford's work by 1911 had so far unearthed only one important building block of the atom—the positively charged nucleus. Scientists now took stock of their inventory of atomic particles that could serve as atomic building blocks. The guiding idea here was to look for charged particles.

There were, of course, the electrons that had previously been discovered in electron tubes. In

1911 the electron could be put on the stock list of atomic particles as a well-known item. It had one negative unit of electrical charge, and its weight was almost 2,000 times smaller than that of a hydrogen atom having the standard weight of 1 atomic weight unit.

In searching through their stock lists, scientists were particularly watchful for positively charged particles because the nucleus was also positive. And they found one. It was a particle they had filed away under the heading of "charged atom of hydrogen." It had been in their files since 1886, when it was discovered in the electron tube.

In an otherwise perfectly empty electron tube the only particles present are electrons. If a trace of hydrogen is introduced into the tube, positive particles can be observed. Because their charge is opposite to that of the electrons, they travel in the opposite direction. They are attracted by the negative wire owing to their positive charge, just as the negative electrons are attracted by the positive wire. The positive particles were studied by running them through magnetic and electric fields, as had been done with electrons and radi-

um rays. It was found that they weighed as much as one hydrogen atom each, and they had one positive unit of electrical charge. Their weight was not surprising; they weighed as much as hydrogen atoms because they *were* hydrogen atoms that had been put into the tube in the first place. However, because they were electrically charged, they were filed away under this heading.

Now, the positively charged hydrogen atom had been standing on the side lines while uranium and radium occupied scientific attention. After the discovery of the atomic nucleus, scientists took a second look at the charged hydrogen atom. If, they reasoned, one negative electron was added to this atom, the electrical charges would cancel and we would get a normal, electrically neutral hydrogen atom exactly like the ones we find in Nature. Adding the light electron wouldn't appreciably change its weight. Could it be that the particle known as the charged hydrogen atom was nothing else but the nucleus of the hydrogen atom?

It was. In fact, the charged hydrogen atom was the most fundamental positive particle that exists.

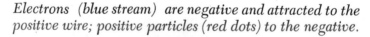

Electrons (blue stream) are negative and attracted to the positive wire; positive particles (red dots) to the negative.

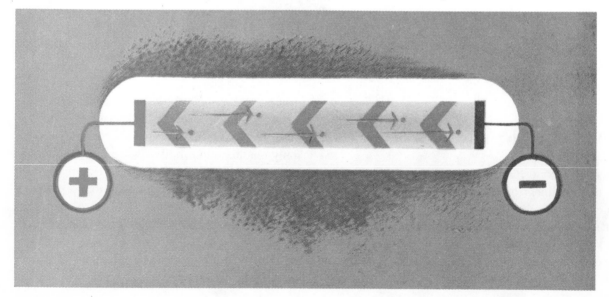

The positive particles were studied by running them through a magnetic field.

It had an electrical charge of one unit and an atomic weight of one unit. In this new light scientists felt that the "charged hydrogen atom" rated a new and better name that befitted its newly discovered importance. It was henceforth called "proton," which mans "primary particle." After all, scientists owed it a flattering name after these long years of neglect.

The proton was assigned the role of the nucleus of the hydrogen atom, the simplest atom in Nature. It was one of the building blocks of this atom. The electron had to be the other, because only then could the proton's charge be canceled without measurably adding to its weight. The two

together produce a neutral hydrogen atom. But where was the electron in relation to the proton? So long as the proton was still filed away under its old name, everybody had tacitly assumed that it was as small or as big as a hydrogen atom. Now that it was assigned the role of a nucleus, it had to be many thousands of times smaller. The electron itself wasn't much bigger. The question then was: How to build an atom—a huge atom, mind you—by using one proton and one electron?

We know that a nucleus is very small in comparison to the whole atom—like a marble in a balloon measuring 300 feet across. These grotesque dimensions we must keep in mind as we

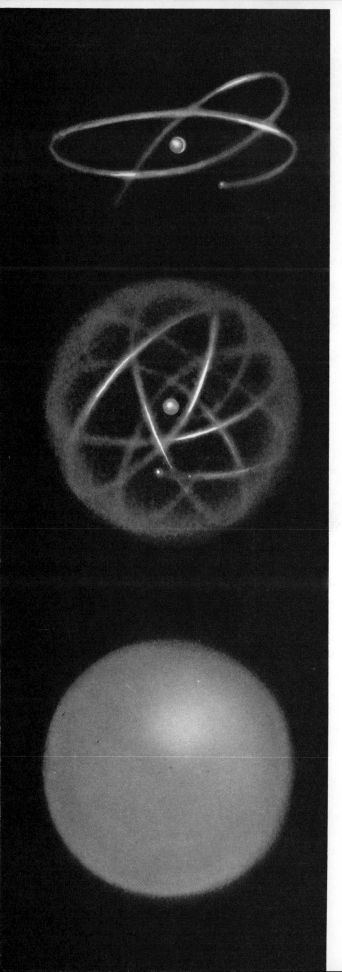

now proceed to build a hydrogen atom from a proton and an electron. Let's try to build it in this large scale so that the weak powers of our imagination are given something to grasp.

If we enlarge a proton and an electron to the size of marbles, we must also enlarge their electrical charge in the same proportion. This is where we run into a fantastic difficulty. For the proton has a positive and the electron has a negative charge. To allow for the proper empty space within the atom, we must place the two charged marbles about 150 feet apart. However, the two opposite electrical charges attract each other. The force of attraction between the two atoms is tremendous. Even over this distance of a small city block they attract each other with the force of 400 million tons!

It is, therefore, utterly impossible to keep the two marbles apart. Even if we filled the 150-foot space between them with a solid wall of high-grade steel, they would bull their way through this wall in their devastating urge to get together. The strength of steel is much too small to resist a force of 400 million tons on an area as small as the cross-section of a marble. The toughest material would behave like butter under this kind of force.

Yet our hydrogen atom *must* be of this size. How in the world are a proton and an electron kept apart by Nature? The answer was given in 1913 by the Danish physicist Niels Bohr.

There exists a famous example of how Nature manages to keep two bodies apart even though they attract each other with an enormous force: the sun and the earth. They attract one another through the force of gravity. However, the earth doesn't fall into the sun, because it constantly swings around the sun in its almost perfectly circular orbit. Things that are swung around a center are subject to what we familiarly know as centrifugal force. Every boy knows this force from playing with a pail of water on a string.

The electron in the hydrogen atom whirls so fast the atom seems to have a solid shell.

A family portrait: each atom can be recognized by the number of electrons it needs to balance the charge in its nucleus—carbon (6), sulfur (16), iron (26), silver (47), gold (79), uranium (92).

The pail can be swung around overhead without the water spilling out. The water is constantly pressed against the bottom of the pail by centrifugal force. Likewise the force of solar gravity is canceled, and the earth is kept at a safe distance. If the earth suddenly stopped swinging around the sun, solar gravity would take over and the earth would be swallowed by the flaming body of the sun after a deadly fall lasting only about two months.

The same principle works in the case of the two attracting particles that make up a hydrogen atom. When the marble proton and electron are reduced to their natural, small size, the force of attraction between them, of course, becomes much smaller, too. But in proportion to their size, the force still remains unbelievably great. You could guess that the electron must whirl around at a terrific speed to offset this force. Bohr has calculated how fast: not less than 7 million billion times in every second!

In its mad dash around the nucleus the electron is, so to speak, everywhere all the time. Whirling around at this high speed, the electron weaves a dense shell all around the nucleus, just as the blades of a spinning airplane propeller form a "solid" disk.

Bohr's theory of the whirling electron solved the problem of how the atom could be so big. It explained how a large atom could be built of two tiny particles. It indicated also how Rutherford's alpha-particle with its great speed could easily penetrate the space covered by the spinning electron, as a bullet can be shot in between the blades of a whirling propeller. If the electron is hit by the alpha-particle, it is pushed aside like a ping-pong ball by a cannon ball. In shooting atoms with alpha-particles one scores a "hit" only if the bullet happens to come close to the hard, heavy nucleus inside the atom.

If a lot of hydrogen atoms are put together inside a bottle, they behave like normal atoms. The electrons in the atoms, with their fast spinning motion, "defend" the space they cover. When two atoms collide, the nuclei never come into contact; the whirling electrons prevent the atoms from penetrating each other. In this sense the electron makes the atom *act* like a hard little ball.

Hydrogen is the simplest atom. It has as its nucleus one proton with one positive charge. It was soon recognized that other elements have nuclei in which two or more protons are packed together. In a package nucleus with two protons, there would be two positive charges. However, Nature always tries to keep an electrical balance in her atoms; normally they are electrically neutral. To offset the two positive charges in the package nucleus, there would have to be two whirling electrons, forming the atom's shell.

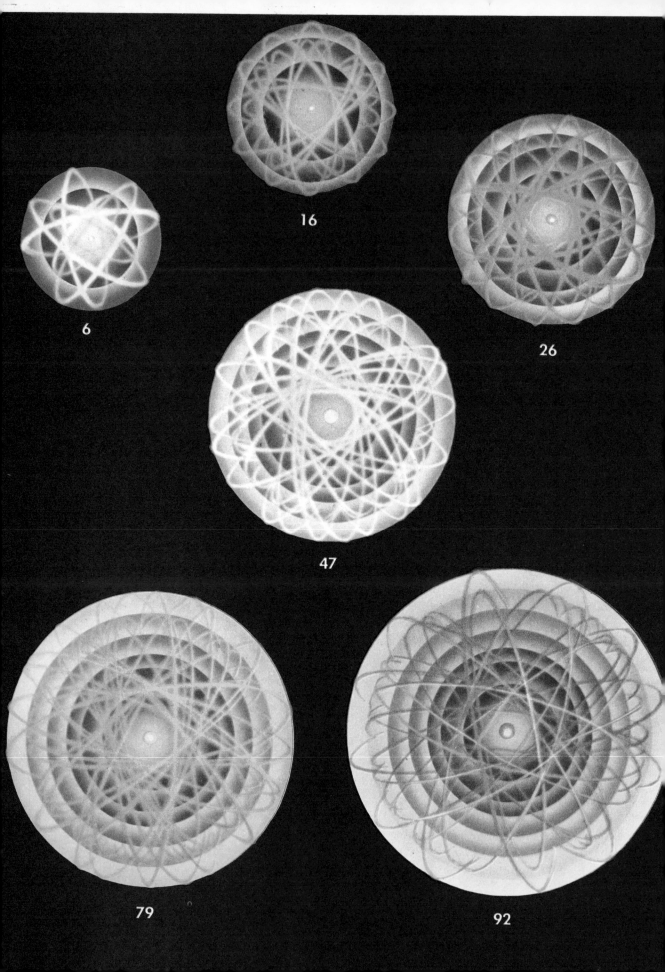

Each atom is recognized by the number of electrons it needs—carbon (6), sulfur (16), iron (26), silver (47), gold (79), and uranium (92).

Atoms with two positive charges in the nucleus and two whirling electrons do exist. They are atoms of the chemical element helium—a light gas used for filling balloons. The hydrogen atom is like a sun with one planet; the helium atom is like a solar system with two planets.

To build the atoms of all other elements, we must add more and more positive charges to the nucleus and an equal number of whirling electrons to neutralize the nuclear charge and to build the ever more complicated atomic shells. Three charges in the nucleus and three whirling electrons will give us an atom of lithium, a metal akin to sodium.

For each number between 1 and 92, chemists have found an element. Defining a chemical element has been reduced to the simple procedure of calling a number.

Bohr's idea of the structure of the atom turned out to be very fruitful. Scientists went ahead to explain many facts in physics and chemistry with this new atomic theory. One important discovery was that when atoms join to form a molecule, they do it by sharing electrons of their shells. The nuclei never change in a chemical reaction; they always stay at great distances protected by their shells of electrons.

Bohr's theory gave us the familiar symbol of the atom—a drawing of a tiny solar system. But through Rutherford and Bohr, atomic theory took a very strange turn indeed. The hard, impenetrable ball of the atom turned out to be mostly— empty space! All things around us—the solid chair you are sitting in, your house, the entire earth—everything is virtually empty space, with its widely scattered, forlorn nuclei and electrons. If all the empty space could be removed from a human body—if all its nuclei and electrons could be crowded together into a solid mass—the body would shrink to the size of a tiny grain of sand

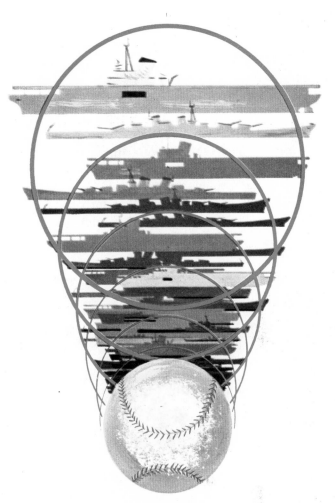

Take away the atoms' empty spaces—and 5,000 ships could fit inside a baseball!

that can barely be felt between the tips of our fingers. Or, take 5,000 battleships and aircraft carriers. If all the empty space in their atoms were removed, all these ships could be crowded into the dimensions of a baseball! But this "baseball" would still weigh as much as all the 5,000 ships. It is horrifying to imagine such an object. It couldn't be kept anywhere. It would sink through the hardest obstacles and probably drill its way to the very center of the earth.

Truly, the atom of Rutherford and Bohr was a dramatically new concept!

67

Exclusive Prey

So THIS is the design of the universe—planets swirling around suns. An outer space filled with millions of galaxies of suns—countless solar systems among them, no doubt. And an inner space —filled with many more countless solar systems of atoms, electrons whirling around nuclear suns.

A universe built of solar systems, infinitely big and infinitely small.

The architecture of the atom was now known and fairly well understood. But science ever progresses. The next step led into the nucleus itself. Like our Fisherman, scientists were curious about the tiny vessel they had netted—the atomic nucleus. And they probed it with every tool of research they could muster.

Again atomic bullets were used. So far, they

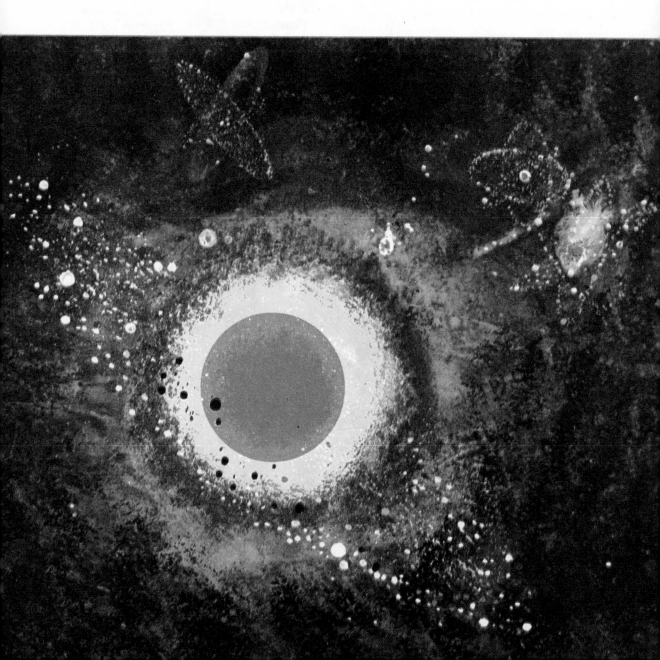

had not touched the nucleus. The available bullets were charged—positively charged like the nucleus itself. We have seen what a tremendous force it is that pulls a proton and an electron together. A force of the same strength acts between the bullet and the nucleus—but in this case it keeps the two apart. Because like charges repel each other, the nucleus was as if cased in almost invincibly strong electrical armor.

Science needed better bullets. But a better bullet was simply a faster bullet. So scientists got busy building huge machines to create faster and faster bullets.

Now, it is fairly easy to strip the electron from a hydrogen atom. In fact, this is what happens in the electron tube. The electron rays that sweep across the tube hit the hydrogen atoms that are put inside. They crash into the atoms and knock the electron out. The naked proton remains. And thereby hangs an important result. For if a proton is put between two metal plates with opposite charges, it is attracted by the negative plate and starts to run for it. If the voltage between the plates is high, the proton picks up great speed. The greater the speed, the better the bullet. And that was what scientists wanted.

Physicists built all kinds of machines that created voltages in the millions. The fast protons that emerged from these high-voltage machines are similar to the powerful radium rays. But they are faster, and there are many more particles in their beams. What comes out of radium or polonium is like a thin trickle, while the proton beams from the machines are like the powerful burst from a firehose.

In thousands of experiments, scientists hurled their artificial rays at the atom. The protons slammed into the nuclei of many elements, and a great number of things happened. Consider, for example, a piece of the metal lithium, which has three charges in its nucleus. It is put at the business end of an atom smasher and shot at with a beam of fast protons. Most of the bullets miss their target because the nuclei are so small, but let us consider one of the protons that happens to be on dead-center. With its great speed it

pierces the electrical armor of the nucleus, crams inward, and gets stuck. The newly created nuclear package now contains 4 charges, and it immediately breaks down into two nuclei of 2 charges each. The new nuclei are helium nuclei, because helium atoms have 2 charges in their nucleus. Thus it is that one element is changed into another.

When scientists started thus to ram their bullets into atomic nuclei, a new field of science was born: nuclear physics. A lot of things were learned during this interesting and important period of the atom smashers. But the prize discovery was made with "old-fashioned" bullets—with the thin trickle of alpha-particles from radioactive elements. They could be used against lightly charged nuclei whose armor wasn't strong enough to ward them off.

For a number of years two German physicists, Bothe and Becker, used alpha-particles in their nuclear studies. One day they selected the metal beryllium as a target. Beryllium is a very light metal closely related to aluminum; its atoms have 4 charges in their nuclei; in the long list of elements beryllium occupies the fourth place, after hydrogen, helium, and lithium. Now, when the alpha-particles slammed into the beryllium nuclei, something baffling happened. For some time nuclear physicists were at a loss to explain it. Finally, in 1932, the English physicist Sir James Chadwick was able to round out the story.

This is what had happened: The alpha-particle with its 2 charges slammed into the beryllium nucleus with its 4 charges. The alpha-particle got stuck, and a nucleus was produced having 6 charges—the nucleus of a carbon atom. But this was not all. The newly created carbon nucleus released a particle that flew away with a great speed. The particle had no electrical charge—it was neutral! This was something entirely new and unexpected. So far all known atomic particles had been electrically charged. Suddenly science found a neutral one, and named it "neutron."

The neutron turned out to be as heavy as a proton. Its atomic weight was also 1. It was like a proton without a charge.

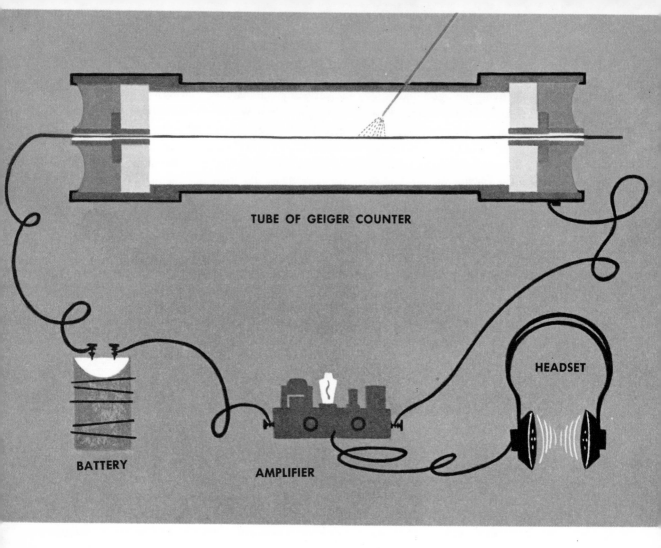

TUBE OF GEIGER COUNTER

BATTERY

AMPLIFIER

HEADSET

The neutron was discovered after more than 20 years of nuclear research. It had managed to escape the hunters this long because it has no tell-tale charge. It is because of their strong electrical charge that protons, electrons, and alpha-particles can be traced easily.

As nuclear physics grew, scientists invented a number of instruments for detecting atomic particles. The flourescent screen was the first device in this line. Later, another radiation detector was invented—the famous Geiger counter, named after the German physicist Hans Geiger.

A Geiger counter is a small metal tube with an insulated wire that runs along its axis. To put the counter into operation, a voltage is put across the wire and the tube walls. The inner space of the tube is filled with a thin gas, so that in its normal state the voltage cannot discharge because of the insulation provided by the gas. Now, an alpha-particle or a proton shoots into the counter. It slashes its way through the gas atoms, and with its strong charge it knocks a number of electrons from the shells of the atoms. The freed electrons make a run for the positive wire. They pick up speed and ram into further gas atoms, knocking out more and more electrons, which in turn also run for the wire; and so a thick avalanche of electrons is created. The avalanche of electrons dives into the wire and causes a small discharge. This is run through an amplifier and transferred to a loudspeaker or a headset. Thus a single alpha-particle or proton snowballs into a shower of thousands and millions of electrons that can be recorded easily. The electric impulse can also be used to trigger a numbered counter drum built like the mileage counter in a car. If a Geiger

70

counter is rigged up in this way, it automatically counts up every single particle.

Only a charged particle can trigger an ordinary Geiger counter. A neutron is without charge, and so it travels straight through the electronic shells of atoms. It exerts no force on the electrons and so cannot knock them out of their places. A neutron cannot start an electronic avalanche by itself.

A neutron can only do one thing. While it travels freely through the inner space of the atoms, it may by chance hit the nucleus of an atom and kick it on its way as one cue ball tees off another. The nucleus then slashes into other atoms and, because it is charged, it triggers an electronic avalanche and makes the counter click. Today neutrons are recorded with counters of a special kind that give them the best possible chance of hitting nuclei; these will then fly off and do the recording for the neutrons. Originally, of course, these special counters didn't exist, and this is why the neutron was able to slip through undetected for a long time. But finally scientists smoked it out of its hiding place in the nucleus.

The neutron was found to be one important building block of the atomic nucleus. The proton was the other. Nuclei are built of protons and neutrons tightly fused to a tiny, dense ball. The only single nucleus in nature is the proton itself, which serves as the nucleus of the hydrogen atom. All other atoms have both protons and neutrons in their nuclei. Helium, for example, has 2 protons and 2 neutrons. All four particles have the same weight of one unit, so that the atomic weight of helium comes out as 4, while the protons give it a nuclear charge of 2. When chemists speak of helium, they use the abbreviated symbol "He." Nuclear physicists are more specific; they write the helium nucleus like this: "$_2^4$He"—weight 4, charge 2. From the two numbers we can see at once that it must consist of 2 protons and 2 neutrons

The next n line is lithium. It is "$_3^7$Li"—3 protons and 4 neutrons. This combination gives a nuclear charge of 3 and an atomic weight of 7. Oxygen is $_8^{16}$O; iron is $_{26}^{56}$Fe. Uranium is $_{92}^{238}$U—it has 92 protons and 146 neutrons in its nucleus. Radium, too, has a crowded nucleus—88 protons and 138 neutrons.

Crowded conditions are the reason why the heavy atoms are radioactive. Their nuclei are "top-heavy," unstable, likely to break apart after a while. By shooting out an alpha-particle they rid themselves of excess weight and excess charge. In a previous chapter we saw how radium (Ra) transforms itself into radon (Rn) when an alpha-particle—or, what is the same, a helium nucleus—is thrown out of the radium nucleus. There is a simple way of saying all this. For this long sentence physicists simply write:

$$_{88}^{226}\text{Ra} - _2^4\text{He} = _{86}^{222}\text{Rn}$$

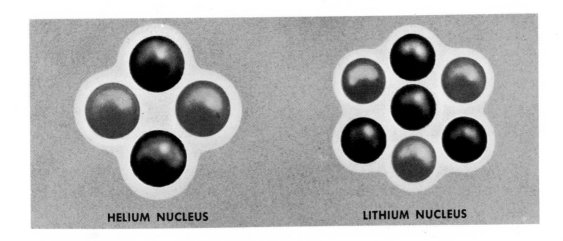

HELIUM NUCLEUS   LITHIUM NUCLEUS

1 Hydrogen H—1 2 1*				
3 Lithium Li—7 2 4*	**4** Beryllium Be—9 1 5*	**5** Boron B—11 2 4*	**6** Carbon C—12 2 5*	**5** Nitrogen N—14 2 4*
11 Sodium Na—23 1 6*	**12** Magnesium Mg—24 3 3*	**13** Aluminum Al—27 1 7*	**14** Silicon Si—28 3 4*	**15** Phosphorus P—31 1 6*
19 Potassium K—39 2 1** 7*	**20** Calcium Ca—40 6 5*	**21** Scandium Sc—45 1 10*	**22** Titanium Ti—48 5 4*	**23** Vanadium V—51 2 7*
29 Copper Cu—63 2 9*	**30** Zinc Zn—64 5 9*	**31** Gallium Ga—69 2 11*	**32** Germanium Ge—74 5 10*	**33** Arsenic As—75 1 14*
37 Rubidium Rb—85 1 1** 16*	**38** Strontium Sr—88 4 13*	**39** Yttrium Y—89 1 14*	**40** Zirconium Zr—90 4 1** 9*	**41** Niobium Nb—93 1 12*
47 Silver Ag—107 2 14*	**48** Cadmium Cd—114 7 1** 10*	**49** Indium In—115 1 1** 14*	**50** Tin Sn—120 10 15*	**51** Antimony Sb—121 2 19*
55 Cesium Cs—133 1 20*	**56** Barium Ba—138 7 12*	**57-71** Rare Earths (See below)	**72** Hafnium Hg—180 5 1** 7*	**73** Tantalum Ta—181 1 1** 12*
79 Gold Au—197 1 18*	**80** Mercury Hg—202 7 12*	**81** Thallium Tl—205 2 4** 14*	**82** Lead Pb—208 4 4** 12*	**83** Bismuth Bi—209 6** 13*
87 Francium Fr—223 1** 8*	**88** Radium Ra—226 4** 9*	**89** Actinium Ac—227 2** 9*	**90** Thorium Th—232 6** 6*	**91** Protactinium Pa—231 2** 10*

RARE EARTHS

57 Lanthanum La—139 2 12*	**58** Cerium Ce—140 4 14*	**59** Praseodymium Pr—141 1 12*	**60** Neodymium Nd—142 5 2** 6*	**61** Promethium Pm—147 16*
62 Samarium Sm—154 6 1** 10*	**63** Europium Eu—153 2 15*	**64** Gadolinium Gd—158 6 1** 10*	**65** Terbium Tb—159 1 16*	**66** Dysprosium Dy—164 7 12*
67 Holmium Ho—165 1 13*	**68** Erbium Er—166 6 7*	**69** Thulium Tm—169 1 15*	**70** Ytterbium Yb—174 7 7*	**71** Lutetium Lu—175 1 1** 12*

This table lists all chemical elements known at this time. The top line in each box shows the element's name and the number of protons in its atomic nucleus—the so-called atomic number. If atomic numbers are arranged in horizontal lines, elements of similar chemical behavior fall periodically into vertical columns as shown by the color scheme. This is why this table is called a "periodic table." The "rare earths" and the "elements beyond uranium" (having atomic numbers greater than uranium)

ELEMENTS AND THEIR ISOTOPES

				2 Helium He—4 — 2, 2*
8 Oxygen O—16 — 3, 4*	**9** Fluorine F—19 — 1, 4*			**10** Neon Ne—20 — 3, 4*
16 Sulfur S—32 — 4, 5*	**17** Chlorine Cl—35 — 2, 7*			**18** Argon A—40 — 3, 5*
24 Chromium Cr—52 — 4, 7*	**25** Manganese Mn—55 — 1, 7*	**26** Iron Fe—56 — 4, 7*	**27** Cobalt Co—59 — 1, 10* / **28** Nickel Ni—58 — 5, 6*	
34 Selenium Se—80 — 6, 11*	**35** Bromine Br—79 — 2, 15*			**36** Krypton Kr—84 — 6, 17*
42 Molybdenum Mo—98 — 7, 7*	**43** Technetium Tc—99 — 15*	**44** Ruthenium Ru—102 — 7, 9*	**45** Rhodium Rh—103 — 1, 13* / **46** Palladium Pd—106 — 6, 12*	
52 Tellurium Te—130 — 6, 2**, 15*	**53** Iodine I—127 — 1, 22*			**54** Xenon Xe—132 — 9, 14*
74 Tungsten W—184 — 5, 8*	**75** Rhenium Re—187 — 1, 1**, 13*	**75** Osmium Os—192 — 7, 8*	**77** Iridium Ir—193 — 2, 12* / **78** Platinum Pt—195 — 5, 1**, 9*	
84 Polonium Po—210 — 7**, 16*	**85** Astatine At—211 — 4**, 15*			**86** Radon Rn—222 — 3**, 13*
92 Uranium U—238 — 3**, 11*				

ELEMENTS BEYOND URANIUM

93 Neptunium Np—237 — 11*	**94** Plutonium Pu—239 — 15*	**95** Americium Am—241 — 10*	**96** Curium Cm—242 — 13*
97 Berkelium Bk—243 — 8*	**98** Californium Cf—244 — 11*	**99** Einsteinium E—247 — 11*	**100** Fermium Fm—254 — 9*
101 Mendelevium Mv—256 — 2*	**102** 102 102—254 — 2*	**103** Lawrencium Lw—257 — 1*	

form special groups of highly similar elements. The middle line in each box gives the chemical symbol of each element and the mass number (protons + neutrons) of its most common isotope. The bottom line shows the number of stable isotopes, the number of natural radioactive isotopes (**), if any, and the number of known man-made isotopes (*) for each element. Element 102 does not yet have an official name because of controversy that still exists concerning its discovery.

73

Nuclear physics thus became a simple, but fascinating, game of numbers!

Protons and neutrons have a way of sticking together tightly to form atomic nuclei. What would happen if a single neutron should stick to a single proton? The two would form the nucleus of a atom with charge 1 and weight 2. This nucleus could string up with a single electron to form a little solar system like a hydrogen atom. Chemically such an atom would behave like genuine hydrogen, because the chemistry of an atom depends only on the number of electrons in its shell. In 1932 this "heavy" hydrogen was found by the American Nobel Prize winner Harold Urey, of the University of Chicago. It is found everywhere mixed up with normal hydrogen. About 1 out of 5,000 hydrogen atoms is a heavy one. In nuclear symbols normal hydrogen is ^1_1H, while heavy hydrogen is ^2_1H.

When scientists took stock of their atoms, they found that there are many with one or even more extra neutrons packed away in their nuclei. Of 10,000 atoms of oxygen, 9,976 will have 8 neutrons besides the 8 protons in their nuclei; but 4 of them will have 9 neutrons, and 20 will even have 10 neutrons. These rare oxygen atoms have an atomic weight of 17 and 18, respectively. But all of them have 8 protons and 8 electrons; this is what makes them oxygen atoms.

An atom does not change chemically if one or more extra neutrons are added to its nucleus. Extra neutrons don't change the charge of the nucleus and, by the same token, the number of electrons in the shell remains the same. The extra neutrons only add to the atom's weight. All these different kinds of atoms belong in the same place in our list of chemical elements, because they have the same number of electrons. Physicists have a special name for atoms that differ only in their number of neutrons; they call them "isotopes," from the Greek word meaning "in the same place."

Most elements are mixtures of isotopes. In fact, only a few elements in nature consist of only one kind of atoms all having the same weight. Others consist of two kinds, like chlorine. Oxygen has three kinds as we have seen—$^{16}_8O$, $^{17}_8O$, and $^{18}_8O$. The metal tin has ten kinds!

With the discovery of the neutron, the last piece of the atomic puzzle was fitted into place. The composition of the nucleus itself was now known. Radioactivity and the isotopes had found their logical explanation. But little did scientists know that their neutron was soon to become the star in a dramatic series of events in science.

The neutron turned out to be the knife by which the Fisherman broke the seal and released the Genie.

$$^{226}_{88}Ra - ^4_2He = ^{222}_{86}Rn$$

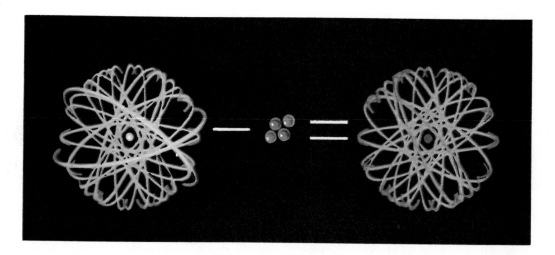

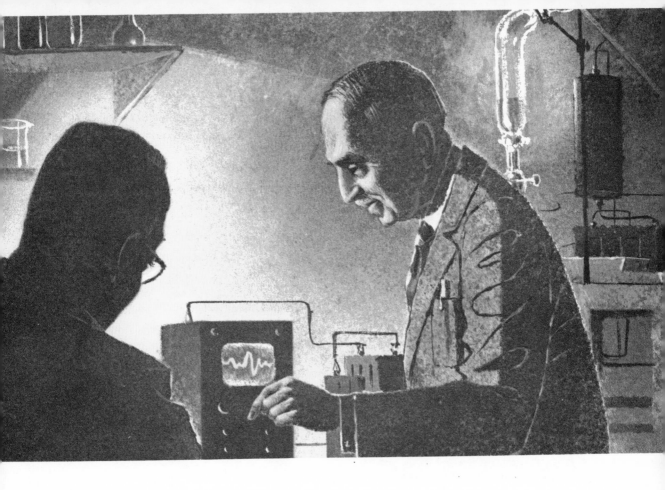

The Atom Splits

YOU WILL recall how, after the alpha-particle was discovered, Lord Rutherford used it in his classic exploration of the atom's interior. The neutron, shortly after its discovery, was used likewise to pry further into the secrets of the atomic nucleus. And what a tool it was!

Having no electrical charge, the neutron is not affected by the negative electrons in the atomic shell. What is more, it is not affected by the strong, forbidding charge of the heavy nuclei. Take uranium, for example, in which 92 protons are crowded together in a small, tight package. A charged bullet such as a proton or an alpha-particle would have to be extremely fast to overpower the strong repulsive force of the 92 protons working together. Before the bullet got near the

nucleus, that force would bring the bullet to a dead stop and hurl it back. A charged bullet, then, has no chance of even touching the uranium nucleus unless it has a tremendous speed.

But the neutron is different. Since it has no charge, there is no force to stop it. It easily floats through the inside of the atom, and if it happens to touch even the most highly charged nucleus, it is swallowed up by the nucleus as readily as a tiny drop of mercury is sucked in by a bigger one.

First to attack the atom with neutrons were the brilliant Enrico Fermi, of Italy, and his co-workers. For a number of years they stuffed extra neutrons into the heavy nuclei of radioactive atoms. Then, in 1935, a group of researchers in Germany also entered this field. Working under the chemist Otto Hahn, director of the Kaiser Wilhelm Institute of Chemistry in Berlin, they concentrated on uranium. Finally, in December 1938, Hahn and his co-worker Fritz Strassmann

75

witnessed a downright sensational event. They split the uranium atom in two!

Hahn and Strassmann were actually expecting something else. In fact, after their discovery they had the wrong explanation for it. Even in their second publication they didn't dare to admit fully what they had found. A short time later, Otto R. Frisch and Lise Meitner, another co-worker and close friend of Hahn, offered the right explanation: nuclear fission.

Radioactive atoms had been known to chip, but not to split. They had been known to break apart by ridding themselves of chips not greater than an alpha-particle—a package of 2 protons and 2 neutrons. These were the biggest pieces that chipped off. But here was something new: the uranium nucleus, on swallowing the neutron, immediately splits, like a glass marble that is dropped on the floor and cracks in two. For an infinitesimally brief moment the two nuclear parts lie side by side. Then—because both fragments

contain dozens of protons that repel each other with a giant force—the fragments are driven apart in a terrific recoil. The tremendous speed is equivalent to an excessive heat—the heat of atomic fission!

A glass marble breaking in two may split in many ways. Rarely are the two pieces equal in size. Uranium nuclei split in a similar way: the fragments vary in size, depending on how this violent nuclear event happens to tear the nucleus apart. The fragments then form all kinds of nuclei. For example, a uranium atom may split in such a way that 56 of its 92 protons wind up in one fragment, while the remaining 36 protons are found in the other. We then get two nuclei with these charges. The first is a nucleus of the element barium, which is akin to calcium; the other is a nucleus of krypton, a rare gas related to helium and neon. There are other ways in which uranium can split and divide its protons: 57-35, 55-37, 54-38, and so on. Mostly, one fragment gets about

A neutron (trail at left) splits uranium atom into barium and krypton. Two neutrons shoot off right.

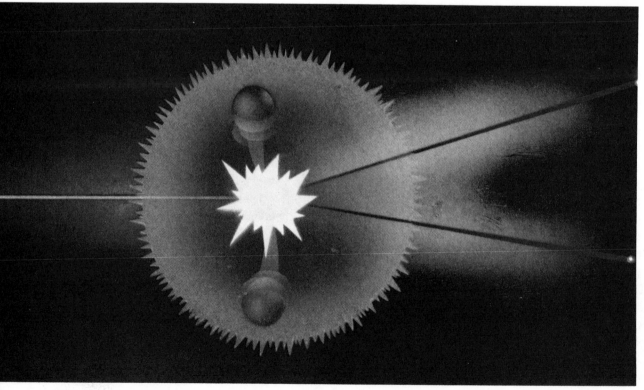

half again as many more protons as the other, even though some nuclei split evenly.

When the nucleus splits, it also gives off an extremely powerful flash of gamma-rays, the penetrating kind of radiation akin to X-rays. But there is still more to atomic fission. When a glass marble cracks in two, you are likely to find a few tiny slivers of glass that have chipped off the sharp edges. In a way, the same thing happens to a nucleus when it cracks; it, too, leaves a few tiny slivers in the process. There are one, two, or even more pieces of nuclear debris falling off when the nucleus breaks. They are single neutrons that fly away from the center of the tiny explosion.

It took physicists only a short time to recover from the shock that atomic fission had given them. They were, of course, greatly interested in studying in detail what nuclei are found among the fragments, and how fast they are driven apart. They measured the intensity of the gamma-rays which the splitting atoms sent on their way. But what fascinated them most of all was the slivers—the neutrons that were discharged every time a nucleus tore apart. These extra neutrons held a fabulous promise: the possibility of an atomic chain reaction. It was the dawn of the atomic age.

Anyone can simulate a chain reaction with a number of mousetraps. A set mousetrap and a uranium atom have one thing in common: both contain trapped energy. You supply the energy for the trap when you bend the spring; Nature supplied the energy when she created the uranium atom, forcing the rebelling protons together in the uranium nucleus and locking them up tightly. Like the coiled spring of the mousetrap, the tense nucleus lies waiting to cut loose. When the mousetrap pops, it is like a uranium atom that splits. The energy is released and the mousetrap jumps up with a sudden start, somewhat as the fragments are kicked apart in nuclear fission.

To make the mousetrap act even more like the uranium atom, we can load it with two ping-pong balls. These are flung away by the popping trap. They are like neutrons that are discharged by the atom when it splits.

With a couple of hundred mousetraps, all set and loaded with ping-pong balls, we can make an excellent demonstration of a chain reaction. The mousetraps, placed side by side on the floor, would represent a small piece of uranium. Now, like uranium atoms, the mousetraps need a trigger to release their energy: one ping-pong ball is enough. Thrown into the heap of traps, the ball will trigger at least one trap. That pops, jumps up, and lets go with its two balls. Now there are two ping-pong balls on their way doing more triggering. They pop two other traps and out come four ping-pong balls. These in turn pop other traps, more balls are flung out, and within a few seconds the whole room becomes a racket of jumping mousetraps and flying ping-pong balls. It is quite spectacular!

This sort of thing is what physicists had in mind when they learned of the neutrons discharged in atomic fission. Could these neutrons not dive into the nuclei of the atoms near by, make them split, and release additional neutrons to split other atoms . . . and so on?

They could do just that.

The result is fantastic. It is terrifying. It takes the mousetraps several seconds to pop. But it takes only a tiny fraction of a second for the millions and billions of atoms to split in an explosive atomic chain reaction. They split at the very same time—as human time standards go. Billions and billions of atomic fragments fly apart with a tremendous speed. A white-hot body of gas is created whose particles tear around with devastating speed. A heat of millions of degrees is created on the spot. It brings forth a monstrous explosion accompanied by an eye-searing flash. Millions of tons of air are pushed aside; a roaring shock wave hurtles in all directions. The billions of splitting atoms combine their bursts of gamma-rays, which penetrate deep air masses. The glowing, suddenly expanding gases leap upward into the high sky, and the devastating updraft forms a billowing, whirling cloud that hangs in the sky like a giant mushroom.

Behind this awe-inspiring cloud we recognize

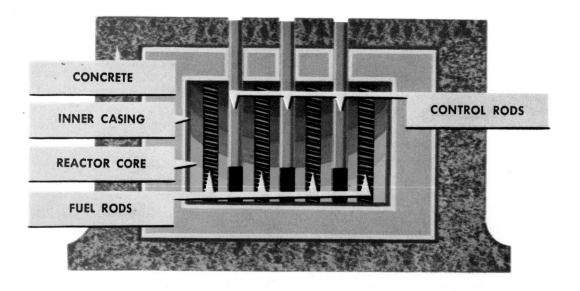

In an atomic reactor, cadmium rods absorb neutrons and slow down the chain reaction

the terrifying form of the Genie of our fable . . . *with eyes blazing like torches, and fiery smoke whirling about him like the simoom of the desert* . . . and his thundering voice promising us death.

When the Fisherman first beheld the frightful form of the Genie, he wished that he had never discovered the vessel. But our fable had a happy ending; the Fisherman had his means of making a friend of his enemy. Fortunately, science has its way of doing the same thing.

An atomic blast is more than a deadly threat; it is also a regrettable waste of energy. Heat and radiations are precious things—valuable assets to our civilization, better used for creation than for destruction. What happens during a split second in an atomic explosion must be slowed down to last for months or even years. Then the atomic Genie will not throw his energy at us in a torrent of heat and radiation; rather he will give us energy as a gently flowing spring gives us water.

79

Atomic physicists produce slow nuclear chain reactions through a special device of nuclear engineering—the famous atomic reactor. It is an enclosed space filled with atomic fuel, usually uranium, whose atoms are splitting in a carefully controlled chain reaction. A number of different types of atomic reactors have been built, differing in design and operation but all having one thing in common: a device to control the speed of the energy-giving chain reaction. The principle of this control device is actually quite simple.

Consider once more our mousetrap chain reaction. It could be slowed down if we employed someone to catch a number of the ping-pong balls and take them out of the game. Fewer balls would remain to pop other traps, and there would then be fewer traps going off in each second. To slow down an atomic chain reaction we must, then, look out for a neutron catcher.

Several chemical elements, among them boron and cadmium, are very efficient at the job. Their nuclei soak up neutrons as easily as a sponge soaks up raindrops. If rods of cadmium metal, for example, are placed so that they can be extended into or withdrawn from the reactor, they will provide effective control. If these control rods are pushed all the way into the reactor, so many neutrons are absorbed that the chain reaction comes to a complete stop. As the rods are pulled out, and more neutrons stay in the game, the rate of splitting increases, and the reactor gets hotter and hotter. The rods work like an accelerator.

In this reactor "pool" water shields the men from stray neutrons.

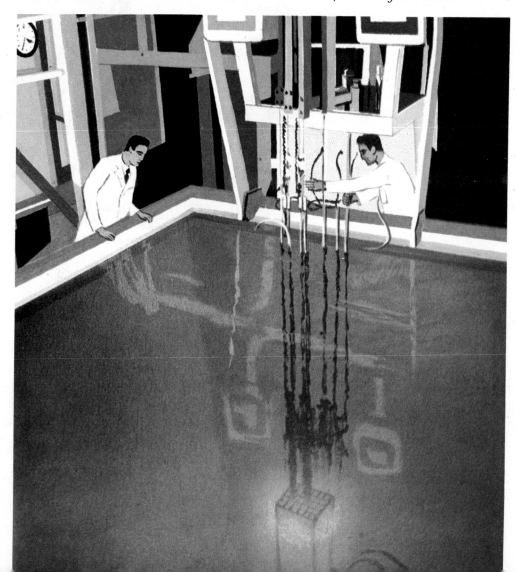

Our First Wish: Power

*The coal and oil resources of our planet
are dwindling, yet we need more and
more power. The atomic Genie offers us
an almost endless source of energy. For
the growth of our civilization, therefore,
our first wish shall be for: POWER!*

DURING the past hundred years we have taken
a giant bite out of our natural fuel resources. Big
though these are, they are dwindling, and every
year the energy demands of the world are increasing. It won't be long, historically speaking,
before we reach the bottom of our pile of cheap
coal and oil. It has been estimated that our reserves will last another 200 or 300 years. But as
early as 1975 even the rich United States will
reach a point where cheap coal from rich deposits
will be scarce; thereafter we shall have to fall
back on low-grade coal. This means that our
fuel bill will go up.

In the perspective of the earth's history, these
prospects are truly alarming. It took Nature mil-

lions of years to create fuel reserves. These treasures were long buried, awaiting the advent of the technical age. Then man started to dig them up—and after a single century he already sees the bottom of the supply. It is as though a thrifty man saved a great fortune over a whole lifetime, and his son comes along and spends it all in a day!

But now there is offered to us a new source of power. The era of atomic power has already begun.

In January 1955, the clean and silent power of the atom pushed a sleek ship of the United States Navy out of the harbor and onto the high seas. The ship's name was "Nautilus," like Captain Nemo's submarine of the immortal tale *Twenty Thousand Leagues under the Sea*. Like its famous namesake, the real "Nautilus" is driven by an inexhaustible source of power. It was the first atom-driven ship of the world.

The prop shafts of the "Nautilus" are driven by a turbine, and the turbine in turn is driven by a beam of hot steam that blasts against its blades. In power plants of this type the steam is produced by atomic energy.

Inside the small reactor of the atomic sub a carefully controlled chain reaction runs its silent course. In every second, billions of atoms are torn in two by billions of neutrons that criss-cross in all directions. The nuclear fragments fly apart and slam into other atoms, causing them to bounce around in all directions. The motion of atoms is heat. Water under pressure is piped through the inside of the reactor and picks up this heat. The hot water is then piped through a tank, where its heat is used to create steam. The steam, in turn, is directed against the turbine blades and drives the prop shafts.

This is only one way of using the heat of an atomic reactor to drive an engine. During recent years a number of different types of atomic power reactors have been developed. Although they differ in design details, they all work with a fluid that is pumped through the reactor core and comes out at high temperature. In some way or another, the heat is transferred to water in the so-called heat exchanger. The heat exchanger has the same function as the boiler in an ordinary steam engine; it becomes the source of steam—the same steam that has been driving the machines of man for more than a hundred years. Only the ultimate source of heat is different. In the conventional steam engine it is a fire of coal or oil; in the reactor it is an atomic fire that drives the engines of the atomic age—engines for locomotion, for mechanical power, and for electricity.

There is a tremendous amount of energy in a little chunk of uranium. While a conventional steam engine must be fed with tons of coal or oil, an atomic power plant runs on a few pounds of uranium. It has been estimated that 20 pounds of uranium could provide enough power to light 25,000 average American homes for a whole year. One pound of refined uranium, ready to go in a reactor as fuel, costs about 35 dollars.

Will energy of the future, then, be as cheap as dirt? Unfortunately, not quite. In a power plant, fuel costs are only one item among many. In nuclear engineering, operating costs are particularly high. Including everything, one kilowatt-hour of electricity produced by the atom still costs more than one kilowatt-hour produced by coal or oil. The "Nautilus," too, could be operated more cheaply on oil than on the atom.

We have been producing power from coal and oil for many years, but we are just beginning to tap the atom's energy. American engineers and business men have the habit of being extremely successful in cutting costs. They will do it again. They will soon bring the atom into line as a competitive source of power.

American industry is determined to make the atom the leading force of the future. The international "Atoms for Peace" conference held in Geneva, Switzerland, in late 1955, was a most optimistic foreshadowing of the coming atomic age. It was conducted in the peaceful spirit of the far-reaching "Atoms for Peace" plan which was proposed in 1953 to the United Nations by the President of the United States.

The Geneva conference was attended by delegates from many nations. The United States was represented by scientists from universities and

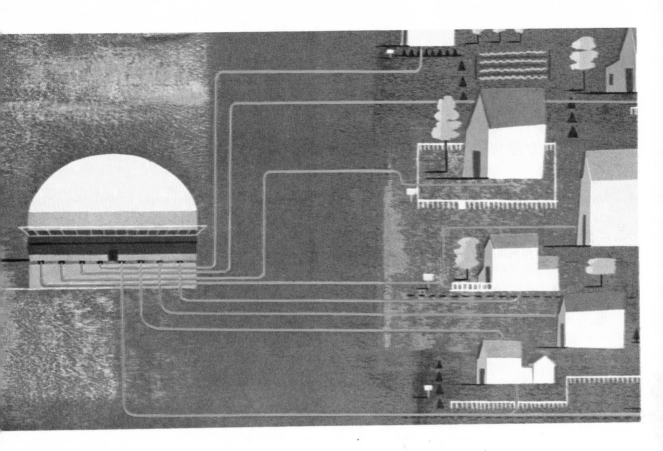

industry, by medical research workers, by industrial leaders, and by experts in nuclear engineering and reactor design. To the scientists of the world this meeting offered a cherished opportunity for exchanging their views, experiences—and their common hopes. And from Geneva there emerged a bright picture of the atom. For the first time the world was shown that the future of the atomic age holds something more than evermore destructive weapons, evermore worldwide dangers from fall-out and radioactive ashes, and the continued threat of the military atom. The hopeful Geneva conference presented the atom for what it actually can be: a powerful force in the service of peace and progress.

In this spirit big corporations in the United States are at present building atomic plants for commercial electric power. There are plans for many more. Near Chicago a huge steel sphere houses an atomic power reactor and a big turbo-generator. This $45,000,000 installation will produce 180,000 kilowatts of electric energy. For New York a $55,000,000 nuclear power plant is

slated to produce 236,000 kilowatts. Britain, France, Russia, and other countries are busy building their own plants. The atom is on its way to light our houses, to toast our bread, to run our television sets and vacuum cleaners. The Atomic Energy Commission estimates that by 1975 about 10 per cent of all the electric power in the United States will come from the mighty atom. Up to now, just about all our civilization's energy has come from the atomic fire in the core of the sun. Soon it will be coming from man-made atomic fires right here on earth.

That does not mean we will soon be driving atom-powered automobiles.

An atomic reactor is still a fairly clumsy piece of machinery that wouldn't fit under the hood of your car as snugly as the sleek gasoline engine of today. And, of course, there is the danger of radiation from the reactor in case of a crash. Atomic power plants are better suited for heavier machines of transportation such as ships. Yet a bulky atomic power plant is still a tight package of power. It runs for months on just one filling.

An atomic merchant ship would have no need for large, space-consuming tanks of fuel and oil; it could call on many ports all over the world without ever worrying about its fuel supply. Whereas in the past many tons of coal and oil have been burned to haul a few more tons of goods from one place to another, in atomic traffic of the future the fuel will be in pounds, but the payloads will still be in tons.

One of the most enchanting prospects of the atomic revolution in the transportation field is the atomic airplane. In aviation, the weight of fuel has always been a discouraging limitation. Only in recent years have non-stop, cross-country flights become routine. The engines of an airplane drain the tanks fast; even our latest planes must make a refueling stop after 8 to 12 hours. In mili-

tary aviation the range of airplanes is extended by means of in-flight (plane-to-plane) refueling— a daring and ingenious operation, but still basically a clumsy method of keeping a plane in the air beyond its normal capacity. An atomic airplane will need no refueling—at least not during the time the crew can possibly stay on the job.

Several aircraft companies in the United States have government contracts for atomic airplanes. They will be different in design to fit different purposes. Probably the first atomic airplanes will be rather large—something like 75 feet long and weighing close to half a million pounds. In existing plans, the atomic power reactor supplies heat. Part of the heat drives a set of turbo-compressors. Great quantities of air, scooped up by broad intakes in front of the power plant, are

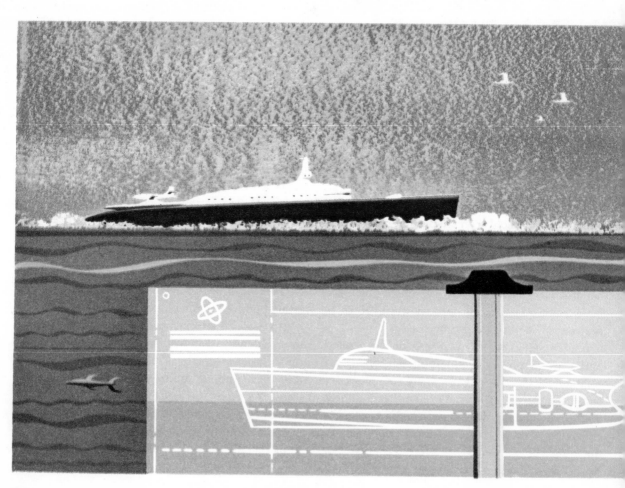

squeezed by the compressors into a special heat-exchanger that heats the air by atomic energy. The hot air escapes as a stabbing jet at the rear end of the airplane. The recoil of the escaping air pushes the plane forward, as in an ordinary jet plane.

The atomic power reactor is encased in a heavy lead shield to protect the crew against dangerous radiations. Crew and passengers are positioned at a safe distance forward of the power plant. The cabin is at the forward end of the ship's big nose. The crew is further protected by plastic shielding and by double-walled windows. The free space between the window walls is filled with water, which absorbs any stray radiation from the reactor.

This heavy plane will need a runway miles long. But once airborne, it will cruise at nearly twice the speed of sound. It will circle the earth many times without ever landing for fuel. It will fly as long as its crew wants it to fly.

And, some day in the future, atomic power will help us to cast off the shackles of gravity that still hold us bound to our planet. The atom will then help us fly freely through the vast reaches of space. . . .

Before the end of this century the atom will largely replace coal and oil as a source of power.

It must! For coal and oil are far too valuable to burn up. They are precious raw materials out of which our chemical industry makes an endless list of useful products—textiles, plastics, dyes, drugs. In the future much of our power will be created inside clean, silent reactors; water power and solar energy will supply the rest.

But how about the resources of uranium—raw material of the atomic age? There is much less uranium on our earth than coal and oil, ton for ton. In each ounce of uranium there is, of course, much more power than in a ton of either coal or oil. It has been estimated that the world's known resources of uranium should give us about 15 times more power than all the coal and oil that still lie in the ground. More will be discovered by uranium hunters. There is, then, a lot of uranium, but our great-grandchildren will want some, too. If our children dig into their supplies as fast as we have, uranium too will some day be short. What then?

We come back to the Einstein equation. It tells

that each piece of matter is a treasure chest of energy. But a splitting uranium atom releases only a tiny fraction of its energy. If the fragments and neutrons discharged in nuclear fission were collected and put together on a scale, they would weigh only a tiny fraction less than the whole uranium atom before it split. Only this minute difference in weight has been converted into energy. It is found in the gamma-ray and in the energy of motion of the fragments and neutrons. All we get out of the uranium atom is a tiny fraction of energy.

Now, we have seen that when heavy atoms come apart, energy is released. With light elements, it is the other way around: they release energy when put together. In exact numbers, 2 protons and 2 neutrons weigh 4.033 atomic weight units. If fused together to form a helium nucleus, they weigh only 4.003 weight units— 0.030 weight units less. This amount of mass is transformed into energy every time a helium nucleus is formed from its component parts.

Obviously this process holds greater promise of inexhaustible energy than the fission of uranium.

Fusion of light elements is what actually happens in the deep core of the sun. This is the secret of solar energy. The fusion occurs in the terrific heat of the sun's core—many millions of degrees. There the protons of hydrogen dash around at tremendous speeds, great enough for them to overcome the electrical forces of repulsion that tend to keep them apart. When they crash into each other, they fuse and form nuclei of helium in several steps. The energy that powers the sun is released in these processes. Slowly the sun uses up its enormous reserves of hydrogen and transforms them into helium. Hydrogen is the fuel and helium is the ash of the sun's atomic fires. But there is enough hydrogen in the sun to last countless billions of years into the future.

Fusion of hydrogen nuclei can take place only at temperatures of millions of degrees. Only then do the nuclei move fast enough to break through one another's electric armor, come into contact, and fuse, releasing energy in the process. This is why physicists call such nuclear fusion a "thermonuclear reaction."

It is from such thermonuclear processes that the hydrogen bomb gets its awesome power. In an H-bomb explosion the high temperature necessary is supplied by a normal A-bomb. In the heat of the initial flash, hydrogen fuses in a blast of incredible proportions. Uranium thus becomes only the trigger for the release of more energy than uranium itself could provide.

The power of fusion has yet to be tamed like the power of fission. So far fusion has been achieved only in the form of the devastating H-bomb blasts that have shaken the very soul of man. Everybody agrees that explosive release of such energy does not belong on this planet. It belongs where Nature first put it: deep inside the stars.

But scientists are not easily discouraged. Some have expressed hopes they will tame the thermonuclear reaction yet.

Our Second Wish: Food & Health

Mankind has long suffered from hunger and disease. The atomic Genie offers us a source of beneficial rays. These are magic tools of research which can, above all, help us to produce more food for the world and to promote the health of mankind. Thus our second wish.

FOR COUNTLESS centuries man has been using fire. He has known that fire can keep him warm, but it can also burn his hand. He has long since learned to harness fire, to put its benefits to use, but to avoid its dangers. With the atomic fire, man faces the very same situation all over again.

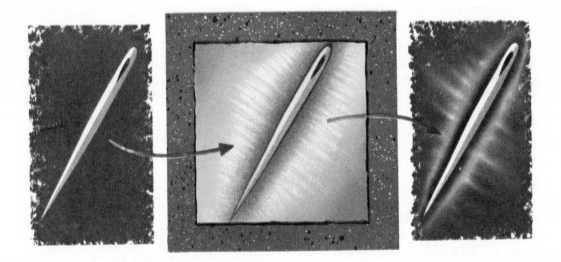

The atom is a source of invisible radiation, whose dangers are infinitely more subtle than those of fire. By the same token, its potential benefits to mankind are also more subtle. The atom's rays hold a great promise for research and medicine.

Inside a reactor is confined a slow, continuous "explosion." It smolders mildly, like softly glowing embers. With each splitting of an atom there is a fierce burst of gamma-rays, and neutrons are constantly produced in great numbers. Both gamma-rays and neutrons are dangerous to man. Undue exposure to these rays causes radiation sickness and shortening of life. To protect personnel working with atomic reactors, the entire core is encased in heavy walls of concrete that absorb the dangerous radiation and prevent it from escaping. Against neutrons, thick layers of water are a good protection. In addition to these basic precautions, all people and equipment are under constant supervision. Medical supervisors monitor atomic installations with Geiger counters to detect stray radiation that could accumulate and become dangerous.

Danger is foremost in our minds when we think of atomic radiation. It makes us forget that the atom's rays have done much good. For many years radioactive rays have been used to treat dread diseases like cancer. Before atomic reactors were built, the only practical source of atomic radiation for medical use was radium. Today the reactor is not only a source of raw power; it is also a device that can be used to make many elements radioactive like radium itself. Since reactors have been in operation, natural radium in hospitals has been largely replaced by artificial radioactive elements.

As we have seen, the neutron is the key to the release of the atom's energy. The same neutron is also the magic wand that turns a normal, natural element into a radioactive one. Here is how it happens:

A tremendous number of neutrons are constantly on the move inside a reactor core. Many million million neutrons fly through each square inch of the core's cross-section in every second. A piece of material sunk into the reactor core is shot through constantly by this dense shower of neutrons. They seep through the atoms of the material as so many millions of raindrops fall through the foliage of a forest. Ever so often a neutron hits the nucleus of an atom and—it gets stuck.

Take the element cobalt, for example. It is a metal closely related to iron and nickel, and one of the few elements in Nature that has only one isotope. All cobalt atoms, as they are found in the earth's crust, are of one kind: $^{59}_{27}Co$—that is, 27 protons and 32 neutrons in the nucleus, giving the atomic weight of 59. If a chunk of cobalt is put into a reactor and exposed to the bombardment of neutrons, a large number of its atoms each capture an extra neutron. These atoms now have 33 neutrons in their nuclei. The new nucleus is written $^{60}_{27}\text{Co}$. A simple equation describes the whole process that takes place in the reactor:

$$^{59}_{27}\text{Co} + {}^{1}_{0}\text{n} = {}^{60}_{27}\text{Co}$$

$^{1}_{0}\text{n}$, of course, is the symbol for the neutron, with its weight of 1 and charge of 0. The newly created $^{60}_{27}\text{Co}$ is still a cobalt atom, because the number of protons in its nucleus has not changed. It is an artificial isotope of cobalt with the atomic weight of 60. Such an atom is not found in Nature; it can only be made artificially.

But this is not all the story. The extra neutron in the nucleus makes the nucleus unstable, like the nuclei of the natural radioactive elements radium and uranium. After a while the cobalt-60 nucleus gives off a gamma-ray. Thus, by putting cobalt in the reactor, we made it radioactive. It is an artificial radioactive isotope—or, as physicists say, a "radio-isotope."

A chunk of cobalt coming out of the reactor contains actually only a small percentage of the radio-isotope cobalt-60. Most of the atoms have not captured a neutron and thus remain normal cobalt-59 atoms. But even these few radioactive atoms mixed up with many more normal cobalt atoms are enough to make the chunk of cobalt strongly radioactive.

The radio-isotope cobalt-60 has a half-life of 5 years and 3 months. After this time half of its atoms have given off their single bursts of gamma-rays, and the radioactivity of the whole chunk of cobalt is exactly one half of its original intensity.

Many other elements can be put into an atomic reactor and made radioactive artificially. A score of radio-isotopes are available today for use in science and medicine. They have opened up a fascinating new area of research and have become one of the most astonishing tools of science in the atomic age. An important aspect of their usefulness is that they can be traced; a Geiger counter will easily tell their presence anywhere,

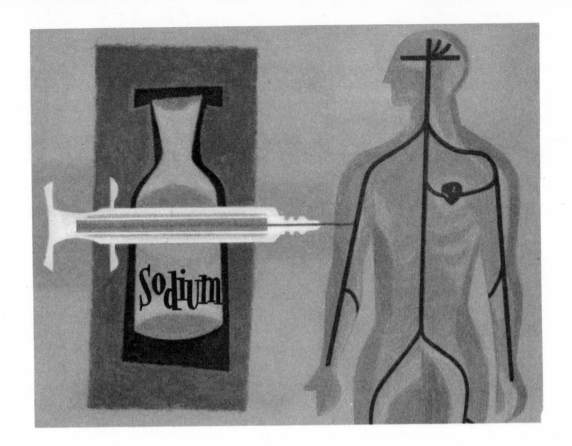

even in amounts too small to be visible or to be traced by ordinary chemical means. This is why radio-isotopes are also called "tracer-atoms."

Take an ordinary needle and put it into an atomic reactor for a short while. Some of the iron atoms contained in the steel will capture a neutron and be transformed into a radio-isotope of iron. When the needle is pulled out, it will radiate mildly. It will cause a Geiger counter to click. Now that needle could be found in the proverbial haystack without any trouble. The Geiger counter would lead us directly to its hiding place.

Making a sample of material mildly radioactive is like putting a bell on a sheep. The shepherd traces the whole flock by the sound of the bell. In the same way it is possible to keep tabs on tracer-atoms with a Geiger counter or any other radiation detector.

This wonderful arrangement makes the radio-isotopes a boon to science, engineering, and medicine. Tracing of small amounts of matter is ex-

tremely helpful in all kinds of research. An engineer, for instance, wants to test how well a new type of piston ring wears. So he mixes up a small amount of iron radio-isotope in the steel and runs the ring in an engine for a few hours. Tiny bits of steel rub off in the process, and there will be a few of the tell-tale tracer-atoms among them. These are washed down into the oil pan. By testing the oil with a Geiger counter, the engineer can tell how much steel is rubbing off—in other words, how well his piston ring wears.

In oil refineries, radio-isotopes can be used to trace oil along the pipe-lines. By adding a few tracer-atoms to the oil, batches of different grades of oil can be "labeled" and followed wherever they go. Hidden leaks are easily discovered; they are betrayed by the presence of radioactivity outside the pipes.

However, by far the greatest value of the radio-isotopes lies in biology. Before biologists had tracer-atoms it was difficult for them to study the chemistry of living organisms. They had to kill their test animals, and plants had to be cut-up. With tracer-atoms they can now study the living body in action. They can follow the movement of matter through the pipelines of life.

So, in the production of food for hungry mankind, the radio-isotopes are potentially a great help. It is very important to know what parts of fertilizers, soils, and soil nutrients are actually taken up by the roots of various plants; the addition of small amounts of radio-isotopes will tell the story. When the plant grows, a Geiger counter will tell how much fertilizer material has actually been used by the plant in building its body. The radio-isotopes can further be traced through the body of an animal that eats the plant. Radio-isotopes, in brief, tell us what the living bodies of plants and animals are doing. Future research with tracer atoms will lead to better crops and will increase the efficiency of our farms. Radio-isotopes will help us produce sufficient food for the increasing population of the world.

Radio-isotopes as used in the human body are bringing about a new era of medicine. They can be used in so many ways that thousands of papers have already been published about them in the medical journals. They are of greatest value in the diagnosis of human disorders, helping in many cases where X-rays fall short. Sodium, for example, can be made radioactive and processed to ordinary salt. In the form of a salt solution the sodium radio-isotope is injected in the arm of the patient; there it is picked up by the blood-stream and transported to the heart. A Geiger counter placed near the heart of the patient will start to click at exactly the moment when the tagged batch of blood arrives at the heart. In this way the blood flow from arm to heart can be timed exactly, offering a valuable clue in the recognition of certain heart diseases.

A patient may have a disorder of the thyroid gland, located in the lower front of the neck. Such a patient is given an "atomic cocktail" containing a small amount of radioactive iodine. Since thyroid tissue has a strong preference for the chemical element iodine, after a few hours most of the iodine radio-isotope has been collected by the thyroid, and there the isotope gives off its tell-tale rays. The patient is then put under a special counter that sweeps slowly across his neck. Measuring the radiation from all directions, a surgeon can map the exact size and location of the thyroid and measure the accumulation of iodine in this gland. Thus although an X-ray of the neck would show nothing, the radio-isotope of iodine may reveal enough for an exact diagnosis of the thyroid condition.

Radio-isotopes can heal, too. Tiny sources of healing radiation can be planted in different parts of the body—to help where radium and X-rays are impractical. Radio-isotopes of gold, for example, are used to cure disorders of the lymph system. Other elements go directly to those parts of the body where they are needed. Phosphorus, for example, is one of the chemical elements of which bones are built, and radio-isotopes of phosphorus therefore collect in the bones. There, its mild radiation works close to the bone marrow, where the body manufactures blood cells. Certain types of blood disease can thus be cured. The radio-isotope phosphorus-32 has a half-life of only $14\frac{1}{2}$ days; so the radiation dwindles and virtually stops after a few months. A patient, then, can carry his own radiation source with him; it does its work all the time, day and night; and after the right dose has been received the radiation dies out by itself.

And there is the radio-isotope of cobalt. We saw that the cobalt-60 isotope has a half-life of more than five years. This is quite long and makes it worth our while to encase a chunk of cobalt in a heavy lead shield and ship it to a hospital. This is the famous "cobalt bomb" which is already in use in many hospitals all over the country. A normal-size cobalt bomb gives off radiation equivalent to three full pounds of radium, but it is much cheaper. It is a bomb built for health—not for death. Carefully controlled amounts of radiation concentrated on a cancer may slow the growth or eliminate it entirely.

Food and health . . . through our second wish we have received the tools to achieve both!

Our Third Wish: Peace

There is left to us the third and last wish. It is an important one that demands wisdom. If the last wish is unwise, then—as some of the old legends tell—all the wishes granted before may be lost.

THE ATOMIC Genie holds in his hands the powers of both creation and destruction. The world has reason to fear those powers of destruction. They could yet destroy civilization and much of humankind.

So our last wish should simply be for the atomic Genie to remain forever our friend!

It lies in our own hands to make wise use of the atomic treasures given to us. The magic power of atomic energy will soon begin to work for mankind throughout the world. It will grant the gifts of modern technology to even the most remote areas. It will give more food, better health—the many benefits of science—to everyone.

We still have much to learn. But the key to a peaceful atomic future lies in the spirit of the great thinkers of the past. From them we have inherited a great wealth of knowledge. Whatever benefits the atom brings us will come from that heritage: the ideas of Democritus, Galileo, Gassendi, and Boyle . . . the work of Lavoisier, Dalton, and Avogadro . . . of Roentgen, Becquerel, and the Curies . . . Einstein, Rutherford, Bohr, Hahn, and many others.

When these scientists created their theories and made their discoveries, they perhaps hardly foresaw that there would ever be widespread application of their work. They simply marveled at the world around them and deeply desired to know about Nature and her ways. That the results of their noble efforts could or even would ever be applied for destruction—this was farthest from their minds and hearts.

They gave us knowledge of the atom, and our last and most important wish will come true if we use the power of this knowledge in their spirit.

Then the atom will become truly our friend.

Ranger Woodlore's Nature Hikes

The Busy Bees

"WHOA! Hold it!" cautioned Ranger J. Audubon Woodlore as he stopped short. He was leading the three duck boys, Huey, Dewey and Louie, down a wooded path. "Something's moving in the bushes over there," he whispered. "Easy now. We don't know what it is . . ."

"A bear?" whispered Huey.

"A mountain goat?" breathed Louie.

"A mountain *lion?*" ventured Dewey, not daring to breathe.

"No," said the ranger softly. "It's a . . . Shh . . . Over to the right a little . . ."

The duck boys stood rooted to the ground, trying not to move a feather. Soundlessly three heads turned and peered to the right. They saw several clumps of brown grass, a few bushes, a great many trees. Not a leaf appeared to be stirring. Not a creature could they see.

Suddenly Huey sneezed. "KACHOO!"

A startled rabbit broke and ran. The boys stared after it.

"Where did it *come* from," gasped Dewey.

Ranger Woodlore chuckled. "It was right in front of your eyes! Right in plain sight! But not moving a whisker and looking just like—just like a clump of brown grass!"

"You mean it has natural camouflage?" asked Dewey. "And that's why we didn't see it, even though we were looking right at it?"

"Right!" replied the ranger. "You've got to learn to *really* see what you're looking at. Keep your eyes open. *Not* your mouths." He frowned at Louie, who was still staring open-mouthed after the vanished rabbit. "Keep your eyes *and* ears open."

Bzz-zzzz-zzz! Something small and buzzy whizzed by . . .

"There it goes!" cried Louie, his quick eyes following the insect as it streaked by. "It's a bee! And it's over by that tree now—the one with the hole in it. Look! It just flew into the hole!"

"Good work, Louie!" said the ranger approvingly. "Know what you've just discovered? A bee tree!"

"Oh, wow!" quacked Dewey. "Let's go over and look in the hole. There's probably some *honey* in there!"

"There probably is," agreed the ranger. "But one thing we're *not* going to do is look in. Bees can sting, you know. And a nosey duck poking around over there could stir up a lot of bees that are equipped to sting invaders of their kingdom. We'll just stay right here at a safe distance, and I'll tell you what's going on in there."

"Like how they make honey?" asked Huey eagerly.

"Yes," said Ranger Woodlore. "But that's just *one* of the many things that bees do. A hive of honey bees all live together in one big busy, buzzy family. The mother is the queen bee. All the rest are brothers and sisters—nearly *all* of 'em are sisters—and they each have a special job to do."

"But where does the honey come from?" said Huey.

"The oldest sisters bring nectar from the flowers," replied the ranger. "Like the bee that just flew by. She was probably carrying home a load

of food from the flowers—nectar in a special tank, to be made into honey and stored in the hive. Besides that, she was probably carrying pollen in special baskets on her hind legs."

"What a load for a little bee!" said Dewey.

"Indeed it is!" said the ranger. "As a matter of fact, a bee can carry its own weight in cargo! No other insect flying machine can do that."

"Oh, look, Ranger Woodlore!" cried Louie. "*More* bees are coming out of the bee tree now. They're making a beeline for somewhere!"

"To the flowers where the food is, I'll bet," said Huey. "They're going to pick up some flower power, aren't they?"

"Right you are," said the ranger.

"How do they know where to go?" asked Dewey. "Did the first bee tell them?"

"Right again!"

"But how *could* she?"

"That's a good question, Dewey," said the ranger. "And the answer is almost unbelievable. The first bee tells the other bees where the flowers are *with a dance!*

"Dancing in a straight line, she tells which *direction* to follow to find the food. Dancing in a circle, she tells *how far away* the food is. She shows this by the speed of her dance.

"But that's not all. She also tells them *how much* food there is. And she does it by shaking her body. The more she shakes, the more food there is!"

96

"That's really communicating!" said Louie. "When she's finished dancing, the other bees know which direction to fly."

"And how many of them need to go," added Dewey, "because she's told them how much food there is to carry back."

"But if they fly in the right direction, they're sure to hit it," said Huey. "So why do they need to know how far away it is?"

Ranger Woodlore looked serious. "Because their lives depend on knowing how far away it is," he answered. "Before leaving the hive, each bee has to tank up on enough fuel to carry her on the whole round trip. If she hasn't enough fuel, she will die on the way. Can you see why?" He looked around at each of the boys.

"You mean she can't eat along the way?" asked Dewey.

"No, she can't," said the ranger. "She has to eat honey, and that's at the hive. She can't pick it up along the way."

"Oh, I see why!" said Louie. "Because the bees make nectar into honey at the hive. And they store it there, too."

"So if a bee leaves the hive," said Huey, "she has to eat enough honey to give her the energy to fly back home. *That's* why she has to know how far she's going, isn't it, Ranger Woodlore?"

The ranger nodded. "And you can see that if she takes *more* honey than she needs, she can't carry home the largest possible load of nectar and pollen."

Dewey was pulling on the ranger's sleeve. "Look," he whispered, "over there on the ground. It's a bird with a broken wing!"

Ranger J. Audubon Woodlore looked. Then he smiled and shook his head. "No, that's mother bird *pretending* to have a broken wing. She's trying to lead us away from her young. Somewhere near is a nestful of helpless baby birds, waiting to be fed. We won't disturb them. It's time we headed for home now anyway."

"I'm starved!"

"Me, too!"

"So it's back to the Little Ranger Nature Camp for us, boys. Our nature hike is over for today!"

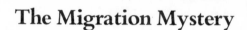

The Migration Mystery

"A great day for a hike, boys!" called Ranger J. Audubon Woodlore. "Where's Louie?"

"Here he comes!"

And down the woodland path came Louie, yawning. "I'm sleepy," he said. "Guess what woke me up early this morning? A woodpecker!"

"They used to wake me up last winter," said Huey. "I thought they'd go away for the summer."

"Birds don't go away for the summer," said Louie. "They go away for the winter, don't they, Ranger Woodlore?"

"Well, that depends," replied the jolly ranger. "If you live down south, then lots of birds go away for the *summer*. They fly north."

"Like the robins," suggested Dewey, "and the wild geese. What's it called when they travel like that?"

"Migration," said Ranger Woodlore.

"But why do birds migrate to a different place?" asked Louie. "For a vacation?"

"Of course not!" replied Dewey. "They do it for really important reasons. To keep warm enough or cool enough."

"Or to find food."

"Or to raise their families in a safe place," put in the ranger. "What time of year are you most likely to see migrating birds?"

"In the fall," said Dewey. "That's when I saw

In late summer, great flocks of monarch butterflies migrate to southern United States.

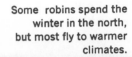

Some robins spend the winter in the north, but most fly to warmer climates.

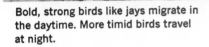

Bold, strong birds like jays migrate in the daytime. More timid birds travel at night.

wild geese migrating. They were flying high in the sky in a big V-formation. It was just before the cold weather began."

"And in the spring," added Louie. "Don't you remember how we saw a whole flock of strange birds here in the woods last spring? The next day they were gone. They were just migrating through, going farther north."

"Birds aren't the only creatures that migrate, you know," pointed out Ranger Woodlore.

"What others do?"

"Well, there's one just ahead of you in that patch of sunlight."

"You mean that butterfly?" asked Dewey. "It can't fly very far, can it?"

"Hundreds and thousands of miles. That's a Monarch butterfly. It migrates in great flocks with others of its kind. Year after year, new generations of butterflies use the same resting places

along their journey. Sometimes they fill whole groves of trees!"

"I wish I could find something that migrates," said Louie.

"Right under your bill," said the ranger. "Look sharp!"

"This grasshopper!" squawked Louie.

"That's right. Ever hear of hordes of invading locusts?"

"Are they grasshoppers?"

"Indeed they are! And the way they start to migrate is very interesting. It seems to happen when the food crops are especially good. The large food supply triggers a grasspopper hopulation—I mean, a grasshopper population explosion. Then the whole crowd starts moving to find more food."

"And that's migration?"

"An invading horde of migrating locusts can

99

light on a field and strip it completely bare of greenery in a matter of minutes!" went on the ranger.

"But suppose," said Huey, "that the field had been planted by a farmer with a crop like, say, wheat. Then the locusts would wipe out his crop! And the farmer and his family would go hungry!"

"That's exactly what has happened countless times," replied Ranger Woodlore. "In fact, it's still happening today in some parts of the world. The trouble is in trying to spot the locust flocks before they eat a hundred miles of scenery."

"Couldn't we do it with airplanes?" asked Louie.

"Yes," answered the ranger. "And we're even doing it with satellites. The satellite travels much higher than a plane and views much larger areas of the earth's surface. With its delicate equipment, it can sense the clouds of locusts as they fly, record their location, and radio a warning to stations back on earth."

"Oh," cried Huey, "I know another kind of population explosion that sets off a migration!"

"What?" demanded his brothers.

"Lemmings!"

"What are *they?*" asked Dewey. "I never saw any."

"They're little animals that live in northern Europe. Every few years when their numbers increase, they start to migrate. And they don't stop until they reach the ocean."

When grasshoppers multiply too quickly, they must migrate in search of food.

"Even then they don't stop," added Louie. "They jump right in!"

"But that's suicide!" quacked Dewey. "I thought that animals migrate to stay alive!"

"Well, the ones that don't make it to the ocean *do* stay alive," said Ranger Woodlore. "And *they* have enough to eat. Which they didn't have before."

"Are there animals in the ocean that migrate?" asked Huey.

"You bet!" answered the ranger. "Fish, crabs, turtles, seals. Even whales."

"Whales migrate?"

"Yes, they migrate from one part of the ocean to another. They swim to where they can find the best food, the best climate, the best places to raise their young. Come to think of it, some creatures migrate right out of the ocean and up the rivers! Salmon do."

"To lay their eggs in the mountain streams where they were born themselves," said Dewey. "I've read about them."

"You're right, Dewey, That's exactly what they do."

"How do they know where they were born?" asked Louie. "How can they remember?"

"That's one of Nature's many secrets that we have yet to discover," replied the ranger. "One theory is that the salmon smell their way back home through the water. They have a keen sense of smell and perhaps a good memory for those smells.

Lemmings start to migrate when food becomes scarce on the tundra.

"An even greater mystery," he went on, "is how certain eels that are born in the ocean always go back to faraway rivers where their parents lived —but where the young themselves have never been!"

"What's an eel?"

"A kind of fish. A very long, thin kind that is sometimes mistaken for a snake."

"Where are the young eels born?" asked Huey.

"In the middle of the Atlantic Ocean," explained Ranger Woodlore. "The eel eggs are laid and hatched in great masses of seaweed there. As soon as they are large enough to swim away, the young eels leave. But by this time their parents are dead, so how do they know where to go? That's the mystery.

"Oddly enough," he continued, "the young eels whose parents came from the rivers of America go back up those same American rivers. Young eels whose parents came from Europe, on the other hand, go back to the rivers of *Europe*. How does each kind find its own special route? Nobody knows."

"Everybody but me has found a migrating creature," said Huey sadly.

The ranger's eyes twinkled. "You're probably standing on one right now."

Huey picked up each of his big feet, one by one. He saw nothing.

"Maybe you'll have to dig for it."

Huey began poking around in the ground with a stick. "Nothing here but earthworms."

"Well?" urged the ranger.

"Do *they* go south in the winter?"

"No," laughed the ranger. "They go *down* in the winter. To get beneath the frost line, so they won't freeze. Then in the spring, they migrate *up!*"

"To meet the robins!" added Louie. "Neat!"

"I'm getting cold!"

"I'm hungry!"

"Let's migrate!"

"Right, boys," said Ranger Woodlore. "Back we go to the Little Ranger Nature Camp!"

Many lemmings drown in the course of a migration.

Salmon travel as far as 2,000 miles to return to the place where they were spawned.

It's Tough to Be a Bird

J. Audubon Woodlore, the little ranger, lowered his binoculars. "Those duck boys have just got to see this," he chuckled. "Where are they?"

He found them in a little clearing in the woods. Huey was shoveling dirt into a hole in the ground. Dewey and Louie were standing quietly beside him.

"What are you boys up to now?" asked the ranger as he hurried toward them.

"We just buried a dead bird," said Dewey. "We found it lying in the grass. Why do you suppose it died, Ranger Woodlore?"

"Hard to say," said the ranger, joining them. "There are so many dangers that threaten them. It's tough to be a bird, you know."

"People shoot them," said Louie.

"True," agreed the ranger.

"We didn't shoot it, Ranger Woodlore! Honest!" said Huey. "We just found it lying there."

"I know you didn't. You boys all know enough not to use living creatures for target practice."

"Maybe an animal killed it," said Dewey.

"Or another bird—like a hawk. They kill smaller birds, don't they, Ranger Woodlore?"

"Yes," said the ranger. "So do owls and shrikes an' crows."

"Maybe it had a disease . . ."

". . . or ate some pesticide," put in Louie.

"What's that?" asked Huey.

"You know—a chemical to kill insects. But it can kill birds and fish and other animals too."

"That's right," said the ranger. "Birds eat the poisoned insects, or fish that have eaten them, and then they're poisoned themselves. A great many birds die this way. We really don't know how many."

"And then the birds aren't around to help eat the insects—so we have more pests than ever," put in Dewey.

"Then the killer of our bird might have been a person that didn't even mean to do it!"

"Yes," said the ranger seriously, "that's unfortunately true. People are killing great numbers of wild creatures without meaning to." He looked carefully at the three boys. "It's really up to all of us to learn the ways of nature. Speaking of which," he added suddenly, "I've got something to show you. Come along!"

Single file behind the ranger, the three boys moved silently through the woods. Ranger Woodlore paused, lifted his binoculars, and then motioned the boys to take a look.

"It's a bird nest," whispered Huey, who was the first to peer through the binoculars. "And there are little beaks sticking up out of it!"

"Wide-open beaks," said Dewey, the next to look. "One, two, three, four of 'em!"

"Hey!" whispered Louie excitedly as he took his turn. "A big bird is feeding them! Stuffing something right down into one of those open beaks! Look!" he added, passing the binoculars back to Dewey.

"It's gone!" said Dewey with disappointment.

"Don't worry," the ranger said. "The other parent will be there in a minute with more food. Some bird parents make two hundred or three hundred trips a day!"

"Who baby-sits with the young birds while both parents are gone?" asked Huey, who was taking another turn at the binoculars.

"Good question," replied the ranger. "The answer is—nobody. And that's one reason that it's tough to be a baby bird. They're quite helpless until they learn to fly."

"I saw a young bird once trying to fly," said Louie, "and it just fell to the ground. The parents couldn't help it at all. They only flew over it, making a big fuss."

"And attracting enemies to the spot, incidentally."

"What about *before* the baby birds hatch—when they're still in their eggs?" asked Louie. "The eggs can get broken or eaten by enemies, can't they?"

"Indeed they can!" said the ranger. "It's especially hard on bird families that lay only one egg a year, as large birds often do."

"Wow!" quacked Louie. "Birds really need all the protection we can give them, don't they, Ranger Woodlore?"

"You're absolutely right!" agreed the ranger heartily.

"What I wonder," said Huey thoughtfully, "is how have birds managed to survive all these dangers?"

"That's the best question yet!" said the ranger. "Fortunately there are lots of answers. Can you think of any of them?"

"Well, they can fly," said Dewey. "None of the other animals can do that! And flying is an awfully good way of getting away from enemies."

"Right you are," the ranger said. "We don't really know how or why flying developed among the early bird ancestors, but apparently it was to get away from enemies. The ones that flew could escape and live to have young that could do the same."

"Different kinds of feet," said Louie, "help birds to do different kinds of things, don't they? Webbed feet help you swim fast."

"Powerful claws help some birds catch fish and other animals for food . . ."

". . . the way eagles and hawks and owls do."

"Some birds eat berries, and their beaks are just right for picking them."

"And some have beaks strong enough to drill holes in trees so they can catch the insects there."

"That's what woodpeckers do."

"How about water birds?" asked the ranger with a smile. "They can strain food out of the water with their flat, toothed bills. And did you know that certain of the sea gulls have a special red spot on their beaks?"

"Oh, yes, and I know what it's for!" cried Huey. "I read about it. It's for feeding the young gulls. The baby birds see it and peck at the spot to get their food from the parent's beak."

"Birds have very good eyesight," said Louie. "I'll bet high-flying birds can see farther than any living creature, can't they, Ranger Woodlore?"

"Yes, I think you're right," agreed the ranger. "By the way, boys, here's an interesting thing. Do you see those two robins over there?"

"I see them," said Dewey softly. "One's a father, and one's a mother robin."

"Exactly," said the ranger. "How can you tell?"

"Because," said Dewey, "the father is brightly colored. He has a reddish breast, and handsome brown flecks on his whitish feathers, and a bright yellow beak. The mother robin is kind of brownish all over. In fact, it's hard to see her at all sometimes, she's so dull-colored."

"Now, here's my first question, boys," said the ranger. "How does the mother bird's coloring help birds survive?"

"Oh, I know!" said Huey. "It's because you can't see her when she's on her nest laying eggs and keeping them warm."

"Good thinking, Huey. Now," continued the ranger, "here's my next question: How does the father bird's bright coloring help the birds survive?"

"I don't know," said Louie. "It seems as if the bright colors would attract enemies."

"We give up," said Dewey at last. "Tell us why, Ranger Woodlore."

"Well," said the ranger, "Louie was quite right when he pointed out that bright colors make the father robin more easily seen by his enemies. But some of his worst enemies are—other father robins! Can you think why?"

The boys looked puzzled. "No, why?" asked Huey.

"It all goes back," said the ranger, "to what we think of as territorial rights. It takes a certain amount of territory to produce enough food to support a bird family. Each father bird knows this. He also knows just how much territory, how much land space, his family needs. So the father robin stakes out his claim and warns all the other father robins to stay out.

"To do this, he makes himself as conspicuous as possible. He sits on the highest branch and calls out his warnings as loudly as he can. The brighter his colors, the more they help to get his message across."

"Lucky for us," said Dewey, "that birds have all these ways of surviving."

"Very lucky for us," the ranger agreed. "We need birds a lot more than they need us!" Then he added with a twinkle in his eye, "Let's head back to the Little Ranger Nature Camp, boys. I've got some bird feeding to do!"

Nature's Better Built Homes

"We're off and running!" cried Louie as he led the way across a sunny field. Behind him, Huey and Dewey picked up speed, while Ranger J. Audubon Woodlore brought up the rear.

"Hold it!" called the stout ranger. "Not so fast!"

But his warning was too late. The next moment Louie fell flat on his face. By the time the others had reached him, he was sitting up.

"Stubbed my toe," he said, looking a little foolish.

"And here's what threw him," said the ranger, pointing to a small hole in the ground.

"What a deep hole!" said Dewey, peering down it. "Did somebody dig it?"

"Yes," smiled the ranger. "A rabbit."

"Well, dig the hole a rabbit dug!" said Louie,

recovered from his fall. "Does a rabbit really live down there?"

"Yes, indeed," replied the ranger. "That's one of Nature's better built homes. It kept the rabbit warm all winter. It's a good place to raise baby rabbits. And a good place to hide from enemies."

"I see an enemy now!" squawked Huey and pointed toward the sky.

Looking up, Louie and Dewey saw it too—a hawk, slowly circling high overhead.

"Wow! Talk about a bird's eye view!" quacked Dewey. "I'll bet he can see anything that's moving down here in this field."

"Lucky the rabbits have their holes to hide in."

"What other animals live underground?" asked Louie.

"Mice," said Huey.

"Prairie dogs," said Dewey. "Remember the prairie dogs we saw once? Each one was sitting by the entrance to his own home, ready to duck down any second if danger appeared. They had

109

tunnels everywhere—a whole apartment house underground!"

"And there's another kind of apartment-house digger right by your foot," added the sharp-eyed ranger.

"You mean those ants?" said Dewey. "Oh, that's right. They dig tunnel houses too, don't they? Look, Ranger Woodlore! What are those little white packages they're carrying?"

The ranger peered closely at a line of ants scurrying under a log. "Those white packages," he said, "are pupa cases. Inside each one is a young, helpless ant, not yet ready to hatch. The older ants are carrying them to a place of safety. Apparently their home has been destroyed."

"And here it is!" cried Huey. He had followed the line of ants back to their starting place. "It's this old, rotten stump here. See how it's been smashed? No wonder the ants are leaving!"

"Nature's better built homes sometimes meet with accidents," said the ranger. "In that case, the best thing to do is to build a new one as quickly as possible. That's what the ants are doing, you see."

"Hey, where's Louie going?" asked Huey, as he and Ranger Woodlore left the smashed stump.

Louie had moved quietly to the trees at the edge of the field. "Shh-h," he cautioned as they followed him. "I've just found a new kind of home—up in that tree!"

The others saw a hole high in the trunk. As they watched, a squirrel popped his head out and then back again.

"Hollows in trees," said Ranger Woodlore, "make some of the best homes. The hollow usually is occupied by the largest creature that can squeeze through the entrance hole. In that way, his larger enemies are kept out—because they *can't* squeeze through."

"I thought squirrels built nests in the branches of trees," said Louie.

"They do," said Dewey. "I've seen them in the winter after the leaves have fallen. The nest looks like a big pile of sticks and dead leaves."

"Yes," said the ranger, "there aren't always enough hollow trees to go around."

"There's another bigger hole in that tree over there," whispered Huey. "Who lives there, Ranger Woodlore?"

"Maybe a raccoon," suggested the ranger. "If so, he won't come out till dark."

"Somebody's been cutting down trees around here," said Louie. "Here's one, and here are more stumps."

"Good work, Louie," beamed the ranger. "You've found the work of a beaver who's been house-building. That means there's water near."

A short distance away they found a small lake.

"But it's got a lot of brush in it over here," said Dewey.

"That's the beaver's house," explained Ranger Woodlore.

"Where's the door?"

"Under the water. You can't see it from here."

"But how can the beaver breathe if his house is under water?" asked Louie, amazed.

"A very good question," said the ranger. "Actually, it's just the *entrance* to the beaver's house that is under water."

"That's so his enemies can't get in, isn't it?"

"Right you are, Huey," said the ranger. "The beaver's living quarters are above the water line. But they're covered over—hidden and made ene-my-proof by the beaver's genius for building with wood.

"As you've seen," he continued, "the beaver uses whole trees to build with—trunks, branches, and twigs. He knows just how to use each part of the tree. He knows just what size tree he needs. And he knows how to drag it to the water and float it into place."

Suddenly there was a loud *SPLATT*, and a splash of spray on the other side of the lake.

"I saw it!" said Dewey as softly as he could. "I saw the beaver dive into the water! How did he make that loud noise?"

"He hit the water with his tail," said the ranger quietly. "That's how he warns the other beavers that strangers are around. He slaps his large flat, powerful tail on the water. He also uses that remarkable tail in building his house—to pack and plaster mud."

"What I don't understand," said Huey, "is what does the beaver use for an ax to cut down the trees?"

"A good question," replied the ranger. "You know, Nature provides the wild creatures with every kind of tool you can think of. For the beaver, a sharp cutting edge—his teeth!"

"Here's another kind of house!" cried Louie. "The owner's at home, but he won't come out." Louie was crouched beside a tortoise shell.

"No, he won't come out," said the ranger, "as long as you're around."

"Why can't he ever come all the way out of his shell, Ranger Woodlore?"

"Because that shell is fused to his backbone and ribs and other bones. Can you come out of *your* bones?"

At the water's edge, Dewey had made a small discovery.

"There's a little lump of sand here going for a walk under the water," he said.

Ranger Woodlore looked closely and laughed. "Another one of Nature's better built houses," he said. "That one belongs to a young caddisfly. He's inside his cleverly glued-together house of sand grains! And you're right—he *is* taking it for a walk."

"I smell a skunk," said Huey, who was sitting on a hollow log.

"Could be you're sitting on a skunk's house," said the ranger. "Well, boys, this is a good time to head back. We have houses too, you know. And that's the best place to go after one of Ranger Woodlore's nature hikes!"

Fishes of the
Tropical Atlantic

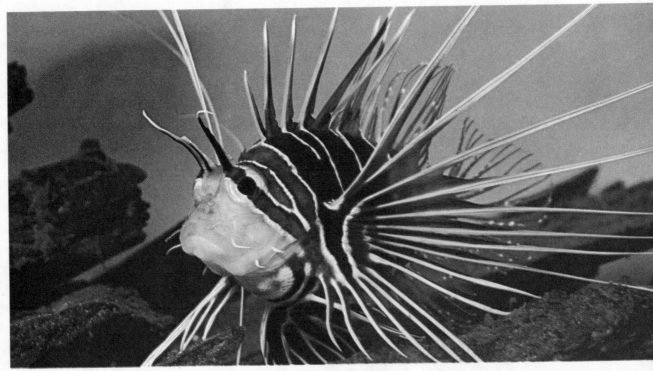

A dangerous beauty, the turkey fish has poisonous dorsal spines.

Warmer waters not only encourage a wide variety of fish but also offer the necessary conditions for the formation of coral reefs. The coral tunnels and cranies offer the ideal place for fish to rest, hide or lay their eggs. Nevertheless the very abundance of life has its disadvantages: each fish must fight for its share of the available food, and predators are readily attracted. Notwithstanding their bright and alluring colors, the usually solitary coral fish keep a constant vigil, and their decorative patterns also provide valuable camouflage.

Of all the fish of the tropical seas, those of the coral reefs deserve special attention because of their immense variety. Nowhere else in the sea do we find such a large number of different species in so small an area. The reason for this is

The upper part of coral reefs in the Red Sea is inhabited by surgeon fish. The species shown here is found only in the Red Sea.

When in danger, the porcupine fish swallows
water rapidly so that its spines become erect.

that the coral reefs provide a tremendous number of sheltered hiding places for the fish.

The open sea is an excellent habitat for countless animals but it has one great drawback: there are relatively few places where an animal can hide or lead a passive life undisturbed. The number of species living in the open sea is therefore infinitesimal in comparison with the number living in a coral reef. The lush underwater weed meadows of these shallow coastal regions house a larger number of species than the open sea since the animals can keep out of sight and attach themselves to a firm support. Similarly, the many holes and crevices of rocky coasts provide shelter for an even larger number of fishes. But the coral reefs surpass them all in the wonderful variety and abundance of fish they support.

The extraordinarily irregular structure of the coral reef provides a maze of caverns, grottoes and tunnels where fish may hide, rest, flee from danger, or lay their eggs.

Apart from this, coral reefs are only formed in parts of the sea where other conditions are especially favorable. They are formed in areas where

The "four-eyed" butterfly fish disguises its true eyes with the black stripe. The black spot near his tail looks like an eye to his enemies.

the temperature of the water never drops below 20°C., where the water is clear, unpolluted by organic or any other waste products, and where all other factors remain constant. Obviously such an environment supports not only an unparalleled number of different species but also an enormous number of individuals of certain species.

The very abundance of life in the coral reefs does, however, result in a few disadvantages:

With its tiny pointed mouth the long-nosed butterfly fish catches little animals among the corals.

117

the animals must defend their homes the more strongly, fight for a share of the available food, and also keep a good lookout for outside dangers —many predatory fishes from the open sea swim into the reefs, attracted by the easy abundance of prey. Consequently, over the centuries the shaping hand of evolution has seen to the development in the animals of the reef community of special characteristics which enable them to survive in their crowded environment.

Many reef fishes have a very slim, laterally compressed body for easy movement among the branching corals, and a long pointed snout for picking food out of small holes and niches. The butterfly fish and the angel fish of the *Chaetodontidae* family are typical examples of this form of adaptation.

Others, such as the hawk fish, have developed into sedentary animals: their swim bladder has disappeared and their pectoral fins have become enlarged to enable them to skip about from ledge to ledge among the corals. The parrot fish has developed very strong jaws to bite off and eat large pieces of coral.

A great many species of reef fishes have developed effective weapons to defend themselves in the struggle for life on the reefs: the surgeon fish, the trigger fish and the porcupine fish are armed with strong spines. Other fishes have poisonous fin rays or spines on their heads and gill-covers.

Many of these characteristics are also possessed by fishes in other environments where life is hard. What, above all, distinguishes the reef fishes from all others is their coloring. Nowhere else do we find such a riot of vivid colors among fish. Biologists studying the reef communities at first concluded that the coral fishes had developed these marvellous colors as a form of camouflage which would protect them by blending with the colors of the corals. But further study has shown this to be unfounded. A few fishes do indeed merge into their surroundings but on the whole the brilliant colors show up as strongly

The bright coloring of the rock beaty, or duke fish, advertises its presence on the reef. The pattern of the coloring, however, disguises its shape from predators.

The prettily marked dwarf bass only reaches a length of about 4½ inches. Other bass species are much larger.

against the contrasting backcloth of the corals as they do against the green glass of the aquarium. Indeed, it looks as if the fish are more intent upon advertising their presence than concealing it. As they swim among the corals each twist and turn of their bodies catches the light in bold color.

Observers have noted that relatively few brightly colored fishes live in shoals. Most of them live alone or with their mate in a home that is fiercely defended. Once the fish has chosen a home or territory, it will fight all trespassers, especially those of its own species—and the flashing of the colors is obviously meant as a warning to other fish to keep away. These fishes remain aggressive in captivity and it is not usually possible to keep more than one specimen in a tank. The only way it can be done is to crowd them into such a small tank that they lose all their natural habits, including the urge to find or defend a territory.

Coral fishes often live together in shoals when they are young and separate at a later stage when they choose a mate. This situation is sometimes reversed, however, and the Caribbean jewel fish is an example. The young jewel fishes have a beautiful dark blue body scattered with iridescent light blue spots. Each has his own territory, defended most fiercely against other fishes of the same species. As the jewel fish matures, its color fades and with it its aggressiveness. By the time

The jaw fish hovers elegantly above its tunnel in the coral floor.

the adult chooses a mate its body has become a dull grey color, keeping only its bright yellow tail fin.

If the bright coloring of the coral fishes serves to advertise their presence as a warning to trespassers, will it not also advertise their presence as a prey for large predatory fishes? This must be so, but on the whole it does not appear to have a noticeable effect on their numbers. There is little difference between the numbers of brightly colored and drably colored fishes caught by predators. If there were, of course, the brightly colored species would either have become extinct

119

The black angel fish has these distinctive markings only when it is young. The fully grown adult loses the stripes and becomes almost completely black.

over the years or would have lost their vividness in the course of evolution.

The reason for their survival in spite of their coloring appears to be behavioral: the very brightly colored solitaries are much more cautious than the duller species living in shoals. The species which live in shoals (including some brightly colored varieties) swim about in a carefree manner, keeping little lookout for marauding predators. They often swim out from the protection of the corals. But the brightly colored solitaries are much more on their guard. They never leave the protection of their territory among the corals and always swim with their bellies at right-angles to the coral, ready to shoot in and disappear among its branches at the slightest sign of danger. Their home is in the center of the territory and from this sanctuary they can keep a lookout without being seen themselves.

While the colors of the coral fishes advertise their presence, the pattern of coloration is usually protective. The most common pattern type is alternating stripes or blotches of contrasting colors running *across* the contour lines of the fish. Examples of this in the tropical Atlantic are the striped butterfly fish, the ribbon fish and the long-nosed butterfly fish. Seen at close range, the colors and outline of the fishes are striking but they protect the fish from enemies a little distance away by disguising its outline. In other words, the color pattern produces an optical illusion which distorts the shape of the fish and makes it unrecognisable as a fish when seen from a distance. Visibility under water is always poor, even in the clear waters of the reefs, and this form of pattern protection is therefore particularly effective.

Another form of color camouflage is shown by the red fish, many varieties of which abound in tropical waters. These fishes are very conspicuous

120

File fishes owe their name to their rough skin, sometimes used as sandpaper by natives.

in aquariums but investigation into their lives in the sea soon reveals the function of their coloring. We find that red fish either become active only at night or live at great depths in the sea. At night, of course, their color does not show, and in deep water the layer of water above the fish acts as a blue filter absorbing the red light rays so that the fish appears black or grey. Their red coloring therefore acts as a camouflage.

Other fishes, including all the flat fish, take on the color and pattern of the surface beneath them.

The sargassum angler is a particularly good example of protective mimicry. It lives among the floating meadows of sargassum weed in the Sargasso Sea and its shape and coloring imitate the weed so closely that it is almost impossible to distinguish which is which.

This strange-looking fish has other peculiarities. Its pectoral fins are set on movable 'arms' and are used to clasp the weeds. It has a movable fishing rod on its head, formed by the first ray of the dorsal fin. The rod is 'baited' by a small wormlike extension which is capable of separate movement. When a small fish approaches, the sargassum angler keeps quite still among the weeds, moving only the 'bait' until the unsuspecting fish gets near enough to be snapped up in its enormous

mouth. Sometimes the angler catches a much larger fish than itself, and its stomach stretches to accommodate such prey. Although its greatest population is in the weed of the Sargasso Sea, the sargassum angler also occurs in small numbers on the coral reefs.

The jaw fish is one of the most remarkable fishes of the Caribbean. It is beautifully colored and although it lives on the sea floor outside the reef it is generally regarded as a reef fish.

Here we see the different stages in the development of the blue head. The three yellow and black striped specimens are young fish; the blue one in the foreground is a mature male.

The royal gramma swims with its belly toward the roof of its underwater cavern. These fish were considered rare until recently, when the secret of their subterranean homes was discovered.

Jaw fish live in colonies in which each individual has its own territory. They dig vertical burrows into the sea floor, grasping and removing in their strong jaws amazingly heavy pieces of coral waste, shells and stones. Larger pieces of coral and shells line the entrance to their homes, which are fairly close together, and one jaw fish often steals a desirable piece of coral from its neighbor in order to decorate or support its own home.

During the day the jaw fish hovers vertically above its home, snapping up planktonic organisms floating overhead. At the first sign of danger it slides down, tail first, into its hole or, when having to flee particularly fast, it dives in head first. After some time it peeps out again to check that all is clear before re-emerging. Toward nighttime each jaw fish in the colony takes a large stone or shell in its mouth, slides backwards into its hole and seals the entrance with the stone or shell, dislodging it again in the morning. Human beings are not the only creatures that lock up before going to bed!

The royal gramma was at one time thought to be a very rare fish. People liked to keep specimens in tropical aquariums but the dealers always asked very high prices for them. Now, however, research with new diving techniques has shown that these fish were rare simply because their habit of living in holes and caverns made them difficult to catch by traditional methods. Once this was known, divers could go down into the holes and catch large numbers of them quite easily.

The royal gramma always swims with its belly facing a fixed surface and thus spends much of its time swimming on its back beneath overhanging parts of the reef and under the roof of its hole.

The carmabi fish are really rare. Only four specimens have been found in the whole world, three by the American ichthyologist, Randall, who donated them to the Caribbean Marine Biology Institute of Curacao. A fourth was kept alive for several years in the Artis Aquarium at Amsterdam.

Cleaning fishes are found in the Mediterranean (*Crenilabrus melanocercus*); in the Red Sea, the Indian Ocean and the Pacific Ocean (species of *Labroides*); and in the Atlantic.

The neon goby is the only true cleaning fish of the Caribbean and tropical Atlantic. Small groups make their homes in a conspicuous part of the reef and hover above them, almost standing on their tails. Reef fishes in need of cleaning swim up to the gobies and signal by their attitude that they want to be cleaned. The gobies then swim out and settle on the sides of the fishes to

The striped butterfly fish has a band of black to camouflage its eyes.

begin nibbling off skin parasites. The fish being cleaned turns on its side and keeps absolutely still, often sinking gradually. The gobies clean the fish quite systematically, often even entering the mouth of a large fish to work over its teeth and gills. The quivering body or shaking head of the customer tells the gobies when it has had enough and they swim quickly away.

The bluehead is not a true cleaning fish. It performs this service in youth only and not in maturity. The young blueheads swim in small groups in a fairly large territory, keeping to no particular spot on the reef. Fishes wanting to be cleaned strike an inviting attitude at the approach of the blueheads which immediately set to work. The neon goby depends on its cleaning activity for food but the young blueheads hunt their own prey in the normal way: the parasites they nibble from their customers are simply tidbits.

Young jewel fishes and angel fishes also clean occasionally, although not as often as the blueheads. The behavior of these fishes may perhaps point to evolutionary steps in the development of the cleaning habit among them: it is just beginning in the young jewel fish and angel fish, further developed among the blueheads and fully formed in the neon gobies.

Reverting once again to the blueheads, we perceive another very remarkable phenomenon, namely the modification in coloring which the male fish undergoes. Many fishes do not take on their adult coloring until they have attained maturity, and this is readily explained by the fact that by this means they are helped to find a mate; by contrast the male bluehead does not take on its final splendor until a very much later stage in its life cycle when it is on the verge of senility, and

The Caribbean squirrel fish is active during the hours of darkness. Its large eyes and red color are perfect adaptations for this life.

A purple squirrel fish. This species is active only after darkness has fallen.

on these grounds therefore the reasons for this change have yet to be adequately explained. Until this point in their lives blueheads, both male and female, are yellow with black lateral stripes along their sides and the change to a full coloring is consequently quite dramatic.

There are, of course, many other species of fish inhabiting the Atlantic and the Caribbean which for their beauty or inherent interest repay study.

Finally we must add a few words in order to explain the relationship of the fauna of the tropical Atlantic to that inhabiting the Indian and Pacific Oceans. The two regions are connected by the waters around the Cape of Good Hope, and at first it may seem strange that so few spe-

cies are common to both regions. When we look at a map of the world, however, we realize that there is a tremendous invisible barrier between them, namely a barrier of cold water. The tropical part of the Atlantic Ocean is surrounded by the cold water of several currents of which the Benguela Current is the most notable: this current reaches the African coast at the Cape of Good Hope, thereby preventing tropical Atlantic fishes from entering the warm waters of the Pacific and Indian Oceans. In view of the impossibility of any tropical fish surviving the cold current, we are amazed at the number of species that are represented on either side of Africa—perhaps because the cold currents were once warmer.

The shape and color pattern of the sargassum angler perfectly imitate the weed in which it lives. Other adaptations are the "fishing rod" on its head and the development of pectoral fins into grasping organs.

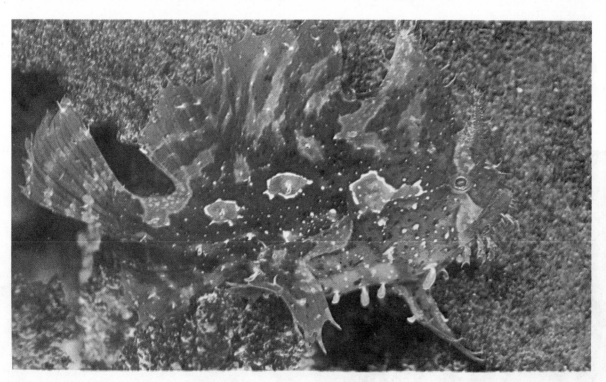

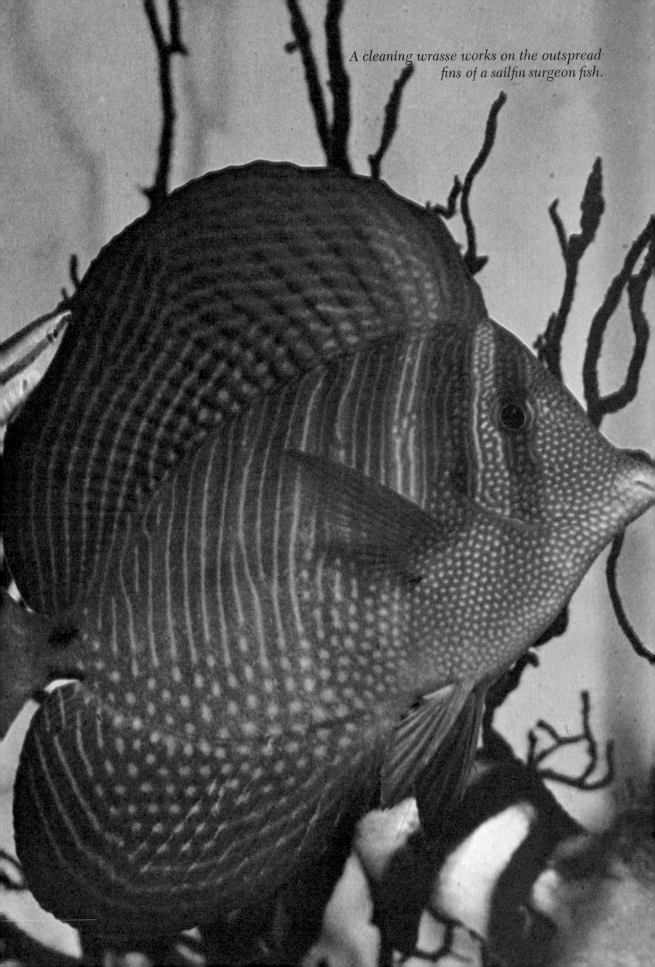

A cleaning wrasse works on the outspread fins of a sailfin surgeon fish.

Walt Disney's Disneyland

They Said It Couldn't Be Done

I N the Minneapolis *Tribune* shortly after Disneyland opened, Will Jones wrote: "If it's an amusement park, it's the gosh-darnedest, most happily-inspired, most carefully-planned, most adventure-filled park ever conceived. No ride or concession in it is like anything in any other amusement park anywhere."

Disneyland, obviously, was never meant to be an "amusement park." The new concept in entertainment dedicated in Disneyland on July 17, 1955, was much more. The Magic Kingdom is a fabulous playground—something of a fair, a city from the Arabian Nights, a metropolis of the future. Above all, it is a place for people to find happiness and knowledge.

When Disneyland opened in Anaheim (27 miles southeast of downtown Los Angeles), it was a 20-year dream come true for its creator, chief architect and head imagineer, Walt Disney. Rough drawings for a "Disneyland" had been found at the Disney studio dating back to the early 1930's, less than five years after Mickey Mouse made his film debut. "I was always trying to think of a place to take my two small daughters on a Saturday or Sunday afternoon—a place where I could have fun too," Walt told the *Reader's Digest*. "At an amusement park the only fun provided for a father, besides having his bottom dropped out from under him on the roller coaster, was the same he enjoyed all week: buying the tickets."

So Walt Disney began to dream, and to plan, a new kind of entertainment center for the young at heart of all ages. But the concept that emerged in the 1950's bore little resemblance to the small park Walt had first envisioned.

Members of his staff recall Walt talking about building an intimate little park adjacent to his Burbank studio. It was to be a "magical little park" two acres in size, with train and pony rides, "singing waterfalls" and statues dedicated to the motion picture characters people throughout the world were already accepting as their own—Mickey Mouse, of course, and Donald Duck, Pluto, Goofy and the rest. It was to be a place to take visitors during tours of the studio and where studio employees might spend relaxing weekends with their families.

The concept never really took hold, however.

For years the "Disneyland" project lay dormant. World War II intervened, and Mickey Mouse, Donald Duck and their friends "enlisted," to star in a variety of training and morale films viewed by millions of GI's. But Disneyland was far from forgotten.

Disneyland was one of those far-out ideas that few people other than Walt Disney believed in. One of those who had faith in the idea was Walt's older brother Roy, president of Walt Disney Productions. *Newsweek* once reported that "to build Disneyland Walt and Roy Disney borrowed to the corporate hilt, and then Walt sold his vacation home at a loss and borrowed against his personal life insurance policies."

Collectively, some of the more indifferent and reserved groups toward the concept of Disneyland were the nation's amusement park owners and operators. Early in 1954, four key members of the Disney staff assigned to develop ideas for Disneyland toured the major permanent amusement parks across America. Recalls one: "We could have paid for the trip with a few dollars from everyone who told us, 'If you don't put in a roller coaster and a ferris wheel, you'll go broke.' Most were completely indifferent—especially the equipment manufacturers who had been building the same whips and shoot-the-chutes for years. They wanted us to buy what they already had, but Walt had other plans. I can only remember two or three of the long-time amusement operators who offered any kind of encouragement at all."

It must have come as a shock to the amusement park men to hear that the baseball throw and the tunnel of love were relics of the past as far as Disneyland was concerned. And to imagine a park without barkers was like thinking of a movie without sound.

In the final analysis, it was television which made Disneyland a reality. Just when all doors appeared to be closed, Walt Disney Productions and the American Broadcasting Company signed a seven-year contract that called for Walt to produce a weekly, one-hour television show. At the studio, its name had already been selected. The program would be called "Disneyland."

Disneyland, the television show, made its debut in the fall of 1954. Disneyland the Park opened less than a year later.

There were many times during those 12 months of construction when the stumbling blocks had appeared insurmountable. One man recalls tagging the orange trees to be retained with strips of red paper and those to be removed with green. A color-blind bulldozer operator began to fell the precious trees marked "save."

A construction supervisor remembers his glow of pride as water flowed into the Rivers of America in Frontierland for the first time . . . then his feeling of desperation as the river promptly leaked its contents into the sandy soil of the former orange grove. Loads of clay soil had to be trucked in to waterproof the leaking river.

With the grand opening of Disneyland just two weeks away, more than 2,500 workmen were swarming over the land in two shifts that totaled 17 working hours a day. In this frantic setting, a television crew began positioning its cameras and rehearsing the scenes that would introduce Disneyland to America. The producer paled and hesitated as his gaze wandered over a scene where clouds of dust billowed and shifted as men and machines toiled. A Disney staff member stepped into the breach. "Don't worry," he comforted, "You'll have plenty of action to shoot. We'll be pouring cement!"

When Disneyland at last opened to an eagerly awaiting public, a mine train pulled out of its station in Frontierland, its load of contemporary pioneers comfortably seated in railway cars designed to recall those that once emerged brimming with silver ore from the mountain tunnels of the west. As the engineer headed his locomotive toward the buttes and rock formations in the distance, he told a little story to his passengers: "A few years ago, this was all row after row of orange trees. Today . . . cactus, snakes, sagebrush, desert. *That's* progress for you!"

A Los Angeles newspaper, quoting an unidentified diplomat, recently reported: "All the crowned heads of Europe want to see Disneyland." Most of them already have: a dozen kings and queens,

18 presidents and prime ministers, 29 princes and princesses, and even a few premiers—with one notable exception. By staying away, that one exception splashed his name, and Disneyland's, across the front pages of newspapers around the world. His name: Nikita S. Khrushchev.

In September, 1960, Disneyland became the center of a *cause célèbre* when the then-Soviet Premier startled millions of televison viewers—and his American State Department escorts—by denouncing the evils of our capitalistic society in a novel way. It had, he said in effect, barred him from having a bit of fun because too many security precautions were necessary before he could visit Disneyland. The "international incident" set off quite a chain reaction:

*Author Herman Wouk wrote a letter: "I don't blame Khrushchev for jumping up and down in rage over missing Disneyland. There are few things more worth seeing in the United States, or indeed anywhere in the world."

*Bob Hope told a joke: "Here we are in Alaska, our 50th state. Alaska—that's halfway between Khrushchev and Disneyland."

*Mr. K. himself soon had an announcement: The Soviet Union, he said, planned to build a "country of miracles" park. Or, as the Moscow park would be called, "Miracleland."

*And in New York City the day following the Soviet Premier's complaint heard 'round the world, an officer of one of capitalism's largest brokerage houses telephoned a Disney executive. The Californian recalls the conversation:

"Maybe you don't remember me," the voice from the east coast said. "I'm the one who said we don't finance 'kiddylands' when you were looking for money to build Disneyland. Now I want to visit your place; if Khrushchev can get so mad over *not* seeing it, Disneyland can't be much of a kiddyland!"

Not an amusement park . . . certainly not a kiddyland. What then *was* the idea behind the creation of Disneyland? And who was qualified to design and shape this new medium of entertainment?

For the team that would help him build Dis-

neyland, Walt Disney turned not to the experienced, skeptical amusement park operators. He turned instead to the field he knows best, motion pictures, and hand-picked a staff of artists, story tellers, machinists and special effects men unique not only for their skills . . . but for their wide-open eyes and minds.

At first consideration, the two mediums—indoor movies and outdoor entertainment—seem incompatible. But an art director who lived those hectic, formative days and nights has a ready explanation: "The basic premise in everything that went into Disneyland was participation, involving people in an experience, and—through that experience—evoking their emotions and stimulating their imaginations. Entertainment is basically an act of communication with an audience, whether that audience is a theater full of people or a mother and daughter in a pirate galleon flying over Peter Pan's moonlit London town."

Several years ago, writing in the New York *Times*, Gladwin Hill described this accomplishment in similar terms: "What is the success of Disneyland? Many factors have entered into it. But to pin-point a single element, it would be imagination—not just imagination on the part of its impresarios, but their evocation of the imagination of the cash customers. Walt Disney and his associates have managed to generate, in the traditionally raucous and ofttimes shoddy amusement-park field, the same 'suspension of disbelief' which has been the secret of theatrical success down the corridors of time . . . In the theatre, the vital ingredient is not realism, but a blending of the real with the imaginary. The entertainer invites the audience to meet him half way. That is what has been successfully achieved at Disneyland."

Writer Ray Bradbury also perceived imagination at work and play in Disneyland. In a letter to the editor published in *The Nation*, Bradbury described his first of many visits to Disneyland: ". . . I did better than take a child; . . . I accompanied one of the great theatrical and creative minds of our time, Charles Laughton. I've never had such a day full of zest and high good humor. Mr. Laughton is no easy mark; he has a gimlet eye and searching mind. Yet *he* saw, and *I* found, in Disneyland, vast reserves of imagination before untapped in our country."

Some have likened Disneyland to a gigantic stage, upon which each guest moves about—seldom a spectator, often an actor participating in the unfolding drama—an integral part of the humor the pathos, the verve of a new "theatre."

Added to the enormous task of blending all the ideas into a basic format for Disneyland was one more that posed the most difficult problem for its creators. Walt Disney wanted everything "new."

"Walt didn't want to build a new concept on old available ride machinery anyone could get his hands on," a construction designer recalls. "Almost everything we undertake in the Park has never been done before."

For example, designers working on the projected Rainbow Caverns envisioned a series of underground chambers with dazzling ribbons of water cascading down the walls of the caverns and flowing in streams of red, green, blue and yellow throughout the caves. To check the practicality of the plan, the artists called in a noted scientist. His report was gloomy. He proved that within a week all the rainbow colors would be but one—water-color gray. Walt listened to this dreary prediction, then turned to his associates and with a characteristic grin gave his own completely unscientific conclusion: "Well, it's kind of fun to do the impossible."

Six months later, the Rainbow Caverns opened at Disneyland. Today, years after their completion, visitors can pick out six distinct colors—none of them gray!

The "Lilly Belle" Grows Up

AN engineer aboard the trains of the Santa Fe & Disneyland Railroad reports that the thunder and lightning storm inside the Grand Canyon diorama has a great many passengers thinking it's for real. "Almost every trip," he reports, "I see five or six people poke their arms out of the train windows to see if it's really pouring."

Imagination again . . . but imagination born out of realism that begins the moment visitors step aboard the trains of the Santa Fe & Disneyland Railroad. The detail and authenticity that characterize Disneyland may be said to take their cue from that railroad.

The *Lilly Belle*, a model train that once huffed and puffed around the back yard of Walt Disney's Holmby Hills home, was the prototype of the most letter-perfect 1890 railroad that ever whistled into a main street station. William McKinley and William Jennings Bryan on the campaign

trail never had it better than the passengers of the Santa Fe & Disneyland taking a grand circle tour of the Magic Kingdom!

The tour includes stops at Frontierland and Tomorrowland, plus a journey through the Grand Canyon diorama. The most striking feature of the diorama is a 306-foot by 34-foot background painting, a seamless, hand-woven canvas that required 4,800 man-hours for painting alone. Appearing in a kaleidoscope of winter-to-spring and sunrise-to-sunset colors, the diorama gives viewers the feeling that they are peering into the Grand Canyon from its south rim.

In the months before Disneyland opened, two trains, an 1890 passenger and a western freight train, were constructed from the wheels and pis-

tons up in the machine shop at Disney studio. Piece by piece, each train was painstakingly designed and assembled. Finely detailed woodwork, metal and iron work and most parts were individually crafted right in the Disney machine shop. The two locomotives built for Disneyland in 1954-55 were a "diamond stack" and a "cap stack," both 4-4-0 engines (they have four wheels in front, four drive wheels, and no trailing truck or tender).

There are now five trains on the railroad. One is pulled by a 70-year-old locomotive that once hauled cane sugar on the Lafourete Raceland and Longport Railway in Louisiana. It was located for the Park by the Railroad and Locomotive Historical Society.

Perhaps the most intriguing aspect of the trains' design was the manner in which scale was determined—and the resulting misconception, existing to this day, regarding the scale of buildings and other structures in Disneyland.

Walt's own *Lilly Belle*, 1/8 of full scale, was first "blown up" in drawings. Then a plywood "mock-up" was built, large enough for a man to walk through. When it was determined that a six foot door was adequate for a human passenger, the rest of the train followed in proportion. The size of the door dictated the size of the roof, the sides, and finally the wheels—36 inches apart on the tracks, or almost exactly the same width as the narrow gauge railroads.

Standard railroad gauge is 56½ inches; Disneyland's 36-inch wheel spread is almost exactly 5/8 scale.

Popular notion is that all Disneyland is 5/8 scale. Actual fact is that only the trains, and some Disneyland vehicles such as the antique autos on Main Street, are 5/8 scale. Main Street itself is several different scales: 9/10 of full size on the first floors of its buildings, and a scale smaller—8/10—at the second story level.

The Dream City

THE real estate boom in a fantasy kingdom recently received a significant boost from a youngster in Peoria, Illinois. Scribbled the youth: "We are planning to move to Disneyland. Can you please send us some booklets about the rides and town?"

Many people have referred to Disneyland as a city unto itself. In a sense, Walt Disney's Magic Kingdom *is* a city . . . one with 4,500 "residents" (permanent and part-time employees) and more than six million visitors each year.

If Disneyland is to be called a city, it is one in which the major form of transportation is an imaginary "time machine." Whenever you step from this vehicle of the mind, you are in another age, another land—each one beckoning you to re-live the era, stories, hopes or dreams that it represents, and to participate in the varied entertainment within its own boundaries.

There are five such individual "kingdoms" within Disneyland: *Main Street, U.S.A.*, small-town America in the period 1890-1910, *Frontierland*, dedicated to the pioneering spirit and boisterous exploits of our fore-fathers, *Adventureland*, "the wonder world of nature's own design," with its jungle boat cruise to far-off lands, *Tomorrowland*, a prediction of things to come on the bold frontiers of the space age, and *Fantasyland*, the "happiest kingdom of them all," where classic stories of childhood have been brought to life.

In the summer of 1954, construction began on this 165 acre "city" in Anaheim. A year later, when Disneyland opened its gates to the public, two million board feet of lumber and 5,000 cubic yards of concrete had gone into its construction, and one million square feet of asphalt had paved its streets and walkways. Giant earth-movers and bulldozers had moved 350,000 cubic yards of earth—enough to build a 20-foot high berm, one and one-eighth miles long around the entire place. "I don't want the public to see the real

world they live in while they're in the park," Walt Disney observed. "I want them to feel they are in another world."

After nearly 20 years, the "magical little park" had become a $17,000,000 magic kingdom. The dream had at last come true.

Main Street

DISNEYLAND'S "time machine" begins to work the moment you walk onto Main Street, U.S.A. The contrast to the hustle and bustle of our modern world and its streamlined modes of transportation is sharp and penetrating. Suddenly, the entire mood changes, and the years roll backward—back to "anywhere in America," circa 1900. And *your* pace slows to match the leisurely clop-clop of the horse-drawn surrey, the um-pa-pa of a band concert in Town Square, the chug-chug of a horseless carriage.

Here once more is another age, rekindling fond memories or bringing to reality a page of Americana that previously existed only in a youngster's history books.

139

"Many of us fondly remember our small home town and its friendly way of life at the turn of the century," said Walt Disney. "To me, the era represents an important part of our heritage, and thus we have endeavored to recapture those years on Main Street, U.S.A. at Disneyland. Main Street represents the typical small town of the early 1900's—the heartline of America."

An art director recalls the philosophy that governed design of this Main Street: "There is a subtle difference between the small towns and large towns of any era. For example, Disneyland's bank and opera house would be out of place in a large city; but in our small town, they are right at home. We were striving to get the most character and flavor into the creation of Main Street. It was much like doing a set for a motion picture. The story-value had to be brought out to put people back in the 1890-1910 period."

There is, however, a not-so-subtle difference between the buildings that line Main Street and a movie set. The latter is to be seen but not touched or entered by the audience; the former is a world of sights and sounds—plus the sensations of touch and smell and the personal adventure of examining, shopping and inhaling the nectar of nostalgia.

From the shelves of Upjohn's apothecary lined with patent medicines that "cure everything from giddiness to trembling sensations," to the "white wing" whose shovel and receptacle were absolute essentials in an age when horses were inviolate (but not necessarily sanitary), Main Street has been authentically re-created.

The design of Main Street is typical of the complete researching that has always been the springboard for a Disneyland attraction. Hundreds of books, pictures and historical items were studied to get the feel of the interior and exterior of stores and shops of the 1900 era. A treasure hunt extended across the country into antique shops, private homes and out-of-the-way junk shops in small villages. The searchers tracked down relics of the past ranging from old lighting fixtures to the hitching posts of yesteryear.

What was found and brought back to Disney-land was the history of another age in bits and pieces. There were 100-year-old gas lamps from Baltimore and Philadelphia, grill work and railings from plantations in Nashville and Memphis, and small park benches from San Francisco.

This treasure contributes importantly to today's living of yesterday in Main Street's attractions, shops and exhibits: bank, bookstore, candle shop, market house, tobacconist, coffee house, ice cream parlor, photo display, registration and information center, china and glassware store, silhouette studio and City Hall. And, of course, the Cinema (silents only) where Rudolph Valentino is still "The Sheik" and hand-tinted slides graciously proclaim "Ladies Over 40 Need Not Remove Their Hats."

On Main Street, the horse and the "gasoline buggy," historic rivals, have become pals. Today teenagers sometimes laugh about "daddy's hot rod" and call the horse-drawn streetcars "hayburning oatsmobiles." But in a land where the skilled touch of the artisan is seen on every side, Main Street's vehicles are truly works of art—in mechanized form.

To re-create a fire engine that might once have answered the alarm in a small village of 1900 America, the studio men designed a chassis, then pored through standard catalogs for unlikely but practical equipment: a jeep rear axle, a three-speed truck transmission, the power plant of a small pick-up truck, standard drive-line parts. To re-create a double-deck omnibus they used only *one* authentic part—an old electric klaxon horn. The drop frame chassis is from a modern day truck, and the bus has both power steering and power brakes! To build-in a slight case of the shakes for the horseless carriages, the designers used today's most efficient two-cylinder water pump engine.

Main Street's old-time autos might delight visitors, but there was a very good chance that they would scare the wits out of the ponies and Percherons who were to pull Disneyland's trolleys and surreys. So, in the weeks before the Park opened, the horses pranced around a circular ring for four hours each day while music, tooting

automobile horns and the laughter and shouts of crowds blared at them from loudspeakers. Amid opening-day crowds, the animals felt right at home.

In an average year, Main Street's vehicles travel more than 23,000 miles, up and down the avenue. Their destination is the Plaza, center of the Magic Kingdom—the stepping-off point for a journey into the many worlds of Disneyland.

Fantasyland

IN medieval times, the drawbridge spanning a castle's moat was purely a defensive safeguard, cranked up to cut off an enemy's entry in time of attack. But when a castle with pink and blue parapets and towers became the entrance into the "happiest kingdom of them all," the drawbridge acquired a new meaning: it became the world's most unusual "welcome mat."

Beyond the drawbridge, in the broad courtyard of Sleeping Beauty Castle, classic stories of childhood are brought to life as adventures in participation for the young at heart. Some are outdoor attractions, for which the designers studied known principles of amusement park rides and adapted or completely revised them for new purposes. Others are Fantasyland's "dark rides," the indoor attractions in which black light, animation, sound and color effects are combined to create some of Disneyland's most beloved and beguiling entertainment.

Two decades of Disney motion picture entertainment provided the inspiration for the dark rides. From "Snow White and The Seven Dwarfs" came a trip through the Enchanted Forest and Diamond Mine. "Peter Pan" contributed a pirate galleon soaring high above the moonlit streets of London Town to Never-Never Land. Haughty caterpillar cars hurtle down the Rabbit Hole into the Upside Down Room, the Garden of Live Flowers, Tulgey Wood, and other settings from Alice's Wonderland. The "hot rodder" of story-book fable, J. Thaddeus (Mr.) Toad, emerges from "The Wind in the Willows" to topple barrels and frustrate policemen along the Road to Nowhere in Particular.

Fantasyland's outdoor attractions include the spinning, people-sized cups and saucers inspired by the Mad Hatter's tea party. Nearby, 72 steeds —each 60 to 80 years old and no two exactly alike —prance gaily to a calliope tune aboard the King Arthur Carousel, largest of its kind in the world. And while the Casey Jr. Circus Train still "thinks he can" climb that steep hill, Dumbo continues to make history as the world's only elephant with aerodynamic ears.

(Long-time Disneylanders still shudder recalling the day a subcontractor delivered the first herd of Dumbos. Specifications called for the elephants to be light-weight "shells" so that the mechanism could lift pachyderm and two guests high into the Fantasyland air. The first ones were indeed "baby elephants"—each weighing 700 pounds!)

The Castle itself is a composite of many medieval palaces, though its designers were probably most influenced by a Bavarian castle. Early drawings of the Disneyland Castle, in fact, looked so much like the German that the facade facing Main Street was extensively re-designed until today both Bavarian and French influences are present.

Though the Castle's tallest tower is but 77 feet above the moat, a device well-known in motion picture circles, forced perspective, has been used to trick the eye into telling the mind that the castle is much taller. The walls and battlements are constructed of stones cut in graduated sizes, from large ones at the foundation to small ones at the topmost sentry posts and turrets.

The same visual trickery has been used in Disneyland's biggest attraction, Matterhorn Mountain. An exact 1/100th scale replica of its Alpine namesake, Disneyland's mountain is 145.6 feet high, but it appears much higher. Up, around and down its concrete and steel slopes (500 tons of structural steel, none exactly the same size) race four-passenger "bobsleds." Climax of a trip down

the mountain is a splash into a pool of water at the base, thrilling the passengers—and stopping the bobsleds.

The mountain is pierced by a series of holes, through which the bobsleds race and trams of the Skyway glide on their airborne journey between Fantasyland and Tomorrowland. According to Disneyland legend, King Baudouin of Belgium is said to have asked Walt Disney why this Matterhorn has holes, and Disney is supposed to have answered, with perfect logic, "Because it's a Swiss mountain."

For perhaps the first time in history, landscapers were called upon to decide just exactly what constitutes "timberline" on a 14-story building. Halfway to the Matterhorn's "snow-capped" summit, they decided, and planted varieties of pine ranging in height from 12 feet at the bottom to two feet at timberline. Forced perspective again.

From the biggest to the smallest in Disneyland is a journey of just a few steps—to Storybook Land. Here European canal boats and the Casey Jr. Train whisk you away to a "kingdom within a kingdom," where the delicate touch of the model maker and the landscaper's inventiveness combine to portray settings in miniature from Disney animated motion pictures.

Model makers at the Disney studio labored six months turning artists' visualizations of Pinocchio's Village, the straw-stick-brick homes of the Three Little Pigs, and other fable favorites into detailed buildings, on a scale of one inch to one foot. They made lead hinges so that six-inch doors would actually open for electricians to change light bulbs. They carved dozens of tiny toys for the window of Gepetto's shop. They installed minute drain pipes and hand-crafted "stained glass" and leaded windows.

Then the landscapers moved in, matching the miniature dwellings by ingenious use of plants and flowers. First they selected plants whose leaf-size was but one-quarter to one-half inch, then they restricted root growth by planting in containers. They met special design problems: they pruned and shaped a three-foot tall Japanese boxwood with gnarled trunk to represent the oak tree where Alice entered the Rabbit Hole. They also uprooted a 100-year-old grape vine, turned it upside down and made it appear like the "terribly tortured old snag" in front of Ratty's home in "The Wind in the Willows."

The most difficult task was in finding live trees that would not *grow* any more, for the forest surrounding the home of the Seven Dwarfs. The answer to the problem seemed to be the Japanese *bonsai* tree. However, these tiny trees require constant care; poor trees were very expensive and good specimens were almost unobtainable. Near Mendocino, in northern California, the landscapers literally unearthed a much more perfect solution. Pine trees truly dwarfed in every respect were growing three to 12 feet in height in a "pygmy forest"—just 50 feet from the same species towering 60 to 80 feet tall! The dwarfed trees had rooted in a limestone shelf; their growth rate is so slow it is nearly impossible to measure. A dozen of these trees now "grow" in Storybook Land, in soil closely matching the nearly sterile conditions of that limestone shelf.

Adventureland

"WALT DISNEY depleted our nurseries from Santa Barbara to San Diego," wrote Hedda Hopper on the eve of Disneyland's opening, and certainly no single project in memory taxed the commercial gardening trade as did Disneyland. Before construction began on the Park, the Disney acreage in Anaheim was almost entirely sandy-soiled orange groves. Today Disneyland is a botanical wonderland. Each year, 500,000 annual and perennial plants and flowers are planted and 1,000 trees transplanted to maintain springtime in the winter and showtime all year 'round. Nowhere is the landscaping more vital than in Adventureland, where a unique combination of living plants and life-like animals has reproduced the atmosphere of the world's tropic regions, from darkest Africa to densest Amazon. Almost overnight, the banks of Adventureland's river were made to overflow with trees, flowers and grasses indigenous to the tropics. Fortunately, southern California is a sub-tropical region; nearly all the jungle plant life was available from major nurseries and private gardens within a 200 mile radius of Anaheim.

Among the most unusual plants growing in Adventureland today are the rare "Bushman's poison," which provides venom for the arrow tips of African hunters; the sacred Bo Tree of India; taro, staple diet of many tropic peoples; and timber-bamboo growing as high as 60 feet. Today the biggest problem for Disneyland landscapers is the same encountered in any untamed land of dense vegetation: controlling the tangle of vines and ferns that make up a true-to-life jungle.

Adventureland's location within Disneyland was selected to take advantage of a row of eucalyptus trees used as a wind-break in the orange groves. Two tall, stately palm trees that once stood before the home of a pre-Disneyland owner, today blend into the tropic motif.

But Adventureland is more than trees and

clinging vines. The Jungle River Cruise is a vicarious exploration for the stay-at-home dreamer, the adventurous spirit lurking somewhere in the hearts of all of us.

Many consider the Jungle River Cruise Disneyland's finest achievement. It compacts into a ten-minute experience the highlights, the *mystique* and excitement of a true-to-life adventure that could only be duplicated through weeks and months spent in the great outdoors. Source material for the designers was, in fact, gathered by photographers who did spend years in Africa—filming the Disney True-Life Adventure, "The African Lion."

Journey with 32 other passengers down tropic rivers, remote and mysterious, aboard bright canopied launches named for the world's waterways: *Mekong Maiden, Irrawaddy Woman, Ganges Gal.* Explore the misty rain-forest of the Amazon, the hippopotamus-filled waters of the Congo, the swirling rapids of the Nile. See a happy herd of elephants, "big shots and little squirts," playfully spraying each other with water and "showering" under a waterfall. Watch the survival of the fittest in the grasslands filled with zebras and lions, jackals and giraffe. See the plight of the "trapped safari," chased up a tree by a snorting, short-tem-

pered, near-sighted rhinoceros, while hyenas laugh their approval.

An Adventureland safari is nearly as wide-ear as wide-eye; for the "native guides" who pilot the boats keep up a constant stream of chatter, part rehearsed and part ad-libbed, but all in the true spirit of adventure and fun. "Please remove your earrings," they warn the ladies. "They attract the head-hunters." Or, "Keep your hands and arms inside the boat—these crocodiles are always looking for a hand-out." And, "Gentlemen, if your mother-in-law is still aboard, you've missed a golden opportunity."

It is the type of dialogue that could be as precarious as a real-life jungle excursion. That it succeeds is a tribute to that unique combination of living plants and life-like elephants, lions, hippos and gorillas—all members of a "cast" which has revolutionized entertainment. Adventureland, with its three-dimensional animated animals, was the laboratory where this revolution began, and continues.

In relative terms, it is a simple task to plan a mechanism for a special effect in a motion picture, one that will do a job once, twice or three times. But to design and build a machine that will produce the desired results and work reliably 12 or 14 hours a day, every day, is quite another story. And Disneyland's animals perform day and night. The jungle animals often startle guests by their realistic appearance and performance. The animals are amazingly complicated. At times, the maintenance crew has been known to say that "these alligators are more trouble than real ones!"

Seen from a front-row seat in a river packet, the Jungle River Cruise is tangible, personal adventure. Viewed from 70 feet above, the twisting waterway is serenity itself. The high vantage point is afforded by the largest of a rare, unnatural species of tree—the *Disneyodendron eximius*, an "out-of-the-ordinary Disney tree." Named for and designed after the Swiss Family Robinson's West Indies domain, its concrete roots penetrate 42 feet into the ground and 300,000 red vinyl leaves "grow" on its branches. Guests who climb to its top (stairs are thoughtfully provided) enjoy not only a wondrous view, but may tour the three-level Swiss Family Robinson tree house, examining the furniture and fixtures used in the parents' room, the boys' room and the delightful open-air "parlor."

A second fantastic *Disneyodendron eximius* towers high above the Tahitian Terrace. The terrace itself is an extraordinary stage setting whose curtain is a cascade of water, and whose footlights are leaping flames of fire burning on the water. The highlight of summer evening there comes when the falls magically draw aside, and from behind the waters sarong-clad natives appear to perform the swaying rhythms and rituals of the islands, the hypnotic barefoot fire walk, or the traditional grass-skirted dances of Samoa, Tahiti and Hawaii.

As they say in the travelogues, this too is Adventureland.

Frontierland

O N a huge sound stage at the Disney studio in 1955, the era of Samuel Clemens' America was being reborn. For the first time in over half a century, a sternwheel steamboat was being built in the United States: a triple-deck paddlewheeler,

appropriately to be christened *Mark Twain*. Soon it would ply a muddy Mississippi of its own, but in the early stages of construction, the riverboat's greatest claim to fame was as real-life proof of an old joke about the man who built a boat in his basement—and couldn't get it out the door.

The *Mark Twain*, 105 feet long, 150 tons and designed to carry 350 passengers, was indeed too big to move through the doors of even the giant sound stage—in its entirety. But this "queen of the river" was rather an unusual vessel: it was the first ever *prefabricated* sternwheeler—built in sections to be dismantled, trucked over freeways piece by piece, and reassembled at Disneyland!

Much of America's history is the story of frontiers awaiting conquest. To Walt Disney, a keen student of history, Disneyland could not be complete unless it told the story of America's pioneer development. As Walt has said, "All of us, whether tenth generation or naturalized Americans, have cause to be proud of our country's history, shaped by the pioneering spirit of our forefathers. It is to those hardy pioneers, men and women of vision, faith and courage, that we have dedicated Frontierland."

Disneyland's frontier stretches from the 1790's to the 1870's, and within the log stockade that serves as its entrance, touches on some of the most colorful aspects of American pioneer history: the boisterous frontier of Davy Crockett, the southwest with its rollicking dance halls, the charm and elegance of early New Orleans, the captivating lure of the ghost towns, and the romance of Tom Sawyer's Mississippi.

Like many a frontier town a century ago, Frontierland is built along a river, the half-mile long "Rivers of America." It was for travel on this waterway that the *Mark Twain* was re-created. Today it is, literally, one of the world's busiest rivers.

Here sails the *Columbia*, exact full-size replica of the first American ship to circumnavigate the globe (1787-1790). Built in Disneyland's own dry dock, this full-rigged, three-masted ship is the first such vessel constructed since the Civil War. It is a marvel of precise craftsmanship, right down to its "dead-eyes" and to the cotton and tar oakum used in hand-caulking its decks.

Here cruise the Mike Fink Keelboats and Indian war canoes that depart from the birch bark longhouse and ceremonial dancing circle of Disneyland's Indian Village. Guided by full-blooded Indians, these canoes furnish Disneyland's most active participation: personal paddling.

Here log rafts float from the mainland to another world—Tom Sawyer Island. Located in the middle of the River, the Island offers an adventure straight out of Samuel Clemens. It is complete with suspension and barrel bridges, Fort Wilderness, balancing and teetering rocks, Injun Joe's Cave and even fishing (for real perch and blue gill, pole and tackle free of charge).

Bordering the river is a composite True-Life Adventure, based on elements of four Disney films, three of them Academy-Award winners. "Beaver Valley," "Bear Country," "The Living Desert" and "The Olympic Elk" provided the inspiration for this seven-acre attraction called Nature's Wonderland. So realistic are the 200 life-like animals, birds and reptiles that the migratory birds which fly over Disneyland have often attacked the animated ravens and owls. With its forest, desert and mountains, with "Old Unfaithful Geyser" spouting water 70 feet in the air, and with its colorful Rainbow Caverns, Nature's Wonderland is indeed the early western wilderness, re-born for a later western civilization.

Tomorrowland

ORIGINALLY, Tomorrowland's goal was to present "a living blueprint of our future." Of all Disneyland's realms, Tomorrowland was the most difficult to conceive and design, and it has undergone the most change. For Walt Disney and his artists were working not in the devil-may-care world of science fiction, but in one based upon conceptions of tomorrow held by some of America's foremost men of science and industry. And in the world we live in, what is tomorrow *today* is seldom tomorrow *tomorrow*.

"Lasers," "fly-bys," "communications satellites" —such terms and the technology to achieve them were unknown in 1954, when Tomorrowland was originally designed. Even the household word "astronaut" was still to be coined. Tomorrowland *has* been a success with Disneyland guests, however. A prime reason is that experts acted as advisors in the precarious business of predicting.

When Walt Disney determined Tomorrowland must have a science-factual flight to the moon, he enlisted two of America's outstanding authorities as the star-gazers: Dr. Wernher Von Braun, then chief of the U. S. Guided Missile Development Division; and Willy Ley, space travel expert.

Several years earlier, in a national magazine article, they had predicted the moon *could* be reached in ten years. Disneyland's simulated space flight, however, was not conceived as a space voyage of one or two astronauts, but rather a scheduled space flight that blasts off at regular intervals, circles the lunar body without landing, and then returns to the safe harbor of Disneyland's Spaceport.

Von Braun and Ley projected such flights *could* be routine by 1980. Taking the basic data they supplied, the Disney staff applied all the skills of motion picture special effects to create the proper moon-scape and in-flight views. Five years later their task would have been immeasurably more simple; in 1954, no film of actual blast-off was available, nor was there photography of the Earth from satellites in space. Every facet of the trip had to be realistically simulated.

Today, in the shadow of an 80-foot rocket ship, space travelers engulfed in sound effects and gently shaken by seat vibration simulating take-off and landing, participate in the early realization of one tomorrow. So accurate have the predictions been that the astounding events of a dozen years have required only the addition of satellites in orbit and "fly-by" space ships.

In Tomorrowland the far reaches of outer space are but moments away from the distant depths of liquid space. On the Submarine Voyage, on a typical Disneyland day, thousands of visitors pass within touching distance of 24-karat gold valued at thousands of dollars. But the treasure in glittering urns and trinkets has its own built-in safeguards: first, it is under ten feet of water and second, it is protected by sharks, octopi, electric eels and even a sea serpent.

The gold is on view in the Submarine Voyage, a $2,500,000 journey to the bottom of the sea, where neophyte mariners chart a course aboard the grey-hulled vessels of, numerically, the world's eighth largest undersea fleet. Disneyland's submersibles, scale versions of America's nuclear-powered navy, sail daily through a South Seas coral lagoon, beneath the Polar Ice Cap, through an under-water earthquake in the Lost Continent of Atlantis, past barnacle-laden Venetian galleys in the graveyard of sunken ships, and into a mermaid lagoon.

To enjoy the vast wonderworld at the bottom of the sea, each of 38 submarine passengers has his own individual porthole. Nearby, to preview the future of mass rapid transit, 106 seated passengers travel at speeds up to 45 miles per hour aboard trains of the Disneyland-Alweg Monorail System.

Early in the planning for Disneyland, Walt Disney expressed interest in a "train of the future" for Tomorrowland. In 1957, following a visit to Cologne, Germany, the engineering staff recommended a design that appeared to offer the best prospects for economy, stability and all-around practicability, not only for Disneyland but for municipal transportation in general. Within two years Disneyland had become the first city in America to introduce a passenger-carrying monorail operating on a daily schedule.

Electrically powered, running on rubber tires over a concrete beamway, a highway in the sky, these almost silent trains immediately captured the public's fancy. Within two years the entire system was extended outside Disneyland for a practical transportation purpose: carrying passengers between the Disneyland Hotel and Tomorrowland's station.

Today the Disneyland-Alweg Monorail System is two and a half miles long, parallels a major highway and crosses a city street. Basic design of its three trains, including power, brake and safety systems, could easily be used in metropolitan transit.

Monorail is a very old idea, not a new phenomenon. Since 1901 Wuppertal, Germany, has had a suspended monorail in which cars ride under the beam—in contrast to the straddling, piggy-back style of Disneyland's. But in an age when urban transit problems are "cussed and discussed" almost daily, Walt Disney was pioneering once again with a showcase for public examination and enjoyment. As an executive of a major transportation company said later, "You've built this entire system in less time, and for about the same money, that my company would allocate for a *feasibility* study!"

How has Tomorrowland, that "living blueprint of our future," fared in practice? In some ways, quite successfully. For one, it has proved to be an ideal framework for displays by American industry. Monsanto's House of the Future indicates a potential new dimension for the use of plastics in housing. The Bell System has used Disneyland for the first major public demonstrations of the picture phone and the family phone booth. Douglas' moon flight has contributed to public understanding of distant space travel.

Tomorrowland has showcased several important new developments. The piggy-back type monorail may have an unlimited metropolitan future. As writer Robert DeRoos said in the *National Geographic,* "Most passengers, myself included, leave the monorail convinced it is the answer for rapid transit of the future."

Circarama, the 360-degree motion picture technique premiered at Disneyland in 1955, has already contributed to an understanding of the U.S. through showings of *America the Beautiful* at the Brussels World's Fair, a United States Exhibit in Moscow, and other fairs. Audiences watch its encircling film from the center of the action so that they may see, almost simultaneously, in front and behind them, and all the scenery in between.

Even the narrow ribbons of roads which make up Autopia's freeways, with multi-levels, crisscrosses and divided one-way lanes, were a prediction of things to come in 1955. Few states in America had an ultra-modern expressway system to match Disneyland's in those days.

When Disneyland opened, experts on road construction and safety no doubt found Autopia interesting. Over the years, however, it is the student of human nature who has been most intrigued by this miniature turnpike system. For, side by side with youngsters gaining their first experience behind the wheel of a real gasoline powered auto, the same adults who grumble and fume about traffic on southern California's full-size freeways plunge happily into Autopia's junior size traffic jams in scaled-down sports cars. Obviously, tomorrow *can* be a wonderful age.

Kings Are Commoners
And Commoners Are Kings

Today the magic of the name Disney and the magnet of the place Disneyland extend from the court rooms of Texas to the gilded courts of Europe's royal families.

In San Antonio, Texas, a prospective juror told the learned judge that he was perfectly willing to serve, but he had already made plans to take his six children to Disneyland. Noting that he had "made a similar commitment for this year," the judge ruled without hesitation: juror excused!

The Louisville (Kentucky) *Courier-Journal* editorialized: "Foreign tourists should not be frightened away by reports of excessive red tape in the United States. It is not true, for example, that a separate visa is required for Disneyland."

The Park has been called "a land where kings are commoners and commoners are kings." Part of this designation is explained by the long list of VIP's numbered among Disneyland's visitors. Kings and Queens who have been guests include Morocco's Mohammed V, Jordan's Hussein, Belgium's Baudouin. Nepal's Mahendra and Queen Ratna, Thailand's Bhumibol and Queen Sirikit, Denmark's Frederick IX and Queen Ingrid, Afghanistan's Mohamed Zaher and Queen Hemaira, and the Shah of Iran. Presidents and prime ministers, several dozen princes and princesses, assorted United Nations delegates, U.S. senators and congressmen, governors, mayors and a full complement of Hollywood stars and their families have visited the Park.

However, the fundamental reason for the king-commoner analogy is found in the basic approach to entertaining its guests that is practiced at Disneyland. Here employees strive to live up to a credo contained in the Park's training manual: "We love to entertain kings and queens, but the vital thing to remember is this: *Every* guest receives the VIP treatment."

Appropriately entitled, "You're on Stage at Dis-

neyland," the training booklet establishes a number of bywords:

"It's not just important to be friendly and courteous to the public, it's essential . . .

" 'Customer' is a bad word.

"We are hosts and hostesses, and *everyone* who enters our main gate is a guest!"

Some Disneyland visitors, however, have had difficulty being just plain guests in the Magic Kingdom. Everywhere motion picture star Betty Hutton went in Disneyland, visitors recognized her and asked for autographs. So Miss Hutton determined to disguise herself. Spying Merlin's Magic Shop in Fantasyland, she purchased a clever concealment—long, false eyelashes, a buccaneer's hat and a special "sword" that appeared to go right through her head. The disguise worked perfectly. No one recognized Miss Hutton. But people continued to stop her. This time they weren't interested in autographs. They wanted to know where they could buy "a hat like that crazy one you've got on!"

The Greatest Show On Earth

IT was old P. T. Barnum who called the circus "The Greatest Show on Earth." In Barnum's day, none could dispute him—the circus reigned supreme. Today, the lure of the circus has paled; the ballyhoo of Barnum has faded into the past. When people talk of "the greatest show on earth," chances are they're talking about Disneyland.

We live in an age of increasing mechanization. Certainly the technology of the space age, applied to entertainment, has been the most fascinating new tool of Disney imagineers over the past decade. But paradoxically, while new animated arts have flourished in Disneyland, the Magic Kingdom has also conceived its own brand of three-ring, something's-always-happening excitement—live entertainment.

Back in 1955, Pepsi Cola's Golden Horseshoe Revue presented a light and gay musical revue. The Disneyland Band tooted in parades and con-

certs. The spaceman quickly became the focus of all cameras. Today, each is still going strong; the Golden Horseshoe, in fact, is America's longest-running show, after more than 18,000 performances. But the contrast between 1955 and Disneyland's live entertainment today is staggering.

On weekend and summer afternoons, mountain climbers scale the Matterhorn. Along Main Street a barber shop quartet harmonizes—aboard a bicycle-built-for-four. In Frontierland Indian dances compete with the guitar-strumming rhythms of a Mexican trio and the jazz of a Dixieland band. In Fantasyland dozens of Disney characters—Mickey Mouse, Pluto, the Three Little Pigs and Big Bad Wolf, Snow White and the Seven Dwarfs—come to life in people-size costumes. In Tomorrowland spaceman and spacegirl greet earthlings, large and small. And back in Frontierland, town marshall and outlaw continue to duel, six-gun style.

On a summer's eve the Fantasy-in-the-Sky fireworks bursting over Disneyland signal the start of southern California's most diverse night life. Dance bands swing out with everything from the twisting, rocking rhythms of the teens to the fox trot, two-beat Dixieland and the swaying melodies of the Pacific Islands. The Park has kept pace with the always-changing trends in teen-age music; the hootenany has found a home here, as have the rousing spirituals of gospel choirs.

Yet Disneyland, on a summer evening, is a mecca for adults, too. Offered the right atmosphere, people will still come out to dance to the big bands. Today, Disneyland presents a whole series of special nighttime events: Dixieland at Disneyland, big band nights, weekend and holiday festivals, and the world's largest New Year's Eve party, where 19,000 annually toast the past and coming years—with non-alcoholic beverages.

For teen-agers, the park has become a date night destination. Special evenings include a frantic Spring Fling and four high school Grad Nights at which 60,000 seniors from 160 schools dance and laugh and cry in all-night celebrations.

But while special entertainment and big name stars often gather the headlines, the newest and biggest everyday star at Disneyland is *Audio-Animatronics*.

So named because it ingeniously combines sound and animation with space-age electronics, Audio-Animatronics made its debut in 1963 in the Enchanted Tiki Room. Here, in a sit-down theater show, more than 225 birds and flowers (none of them alive) and tropic Tiki idols sing, talk, joke and chant in life-like fashion.

Disney technicians have devised a complex way to program movements and record them—along with music, singing, dialogue and sounds—on a single, one-inch magnetic tape. Hundreds of separate actions can be programmed and stored on this tape. When the recorded animation and music is played back, electronic impulses activate air cylinders, pistons, springs and valves inside the figures. Magically, birds talk, Tikis chant and flowers croon.

The Tiki Room would have been an impossibility in 1955, when Disneyland opened. It took the precision techniques and electronic systems of the space age to produce the revue. Or, as one technician puts it, "We've got almost enough gadgets and equipment for this show to put all of Disneyland into orbit!"

Disneyland Will Never Be Completed

WHEN Disneyland opened, Walt Disney told a nation-wide television audience: "Disneyland will never be completed. It will continue to grow, to add new things, as long as there is imagination left in the world."

By the mid-1960's, the park that was "something of a fair, a city from the Arabian nights" had become a $75 million international playground visited by citizens of more than 100 nations, and annually attracting more than six million patrons, over four million of them adults. Originally it had 22 attractions; today there are

more than 50. An entire new land, New Orleans Square, has grown up on the banks of the Rivers of America. Total price tag of these new adventures: more than *three times* Disneyland's initial cost.

Oddly enough, the 1964-65 New York World's Fair, more than 3,000 miles from Anaheim, has brought about more changes in the Magic Kingdom than any other single stimulant.

The story of Disney-at-the-Fair also began at WED Enterprises. There, often side-by-side with new ideas for Disneyland, World's Fair attractions for General Electric, Pepsi Cola, Ford Motor Company and the State of Illinois were conceived and designed.

For two springs and summers in New York, Disneyland-style entertainment captivated eastern audiences. Ninety-one percent of the Fair's paid attendance—46,871,236 people—visited these four Disney attractions.

Today, the story of Disney and the Fair continues. After a two year "road show" in New York, all four shows, in one form or another, are finding new homes in Disneyland. In 1965, the Magic Kingdom unveiled the first of these Fair attractions, "Great Moments with Mr. Lincoln."

Walt Disney has long held the belief, shared by many Americans, that more of us should recognize the influence of historical events on our lives today . . . and the significance of our American heritage in the future development of this nation. That belief motivated "Great Moments with Mr. Lincoln."

Presented in a new 500-seat theater in Town Square's Opera House, this stirring dramatization has at its heart the three-dimensional figure of Abraham Lincoln.

The Lincoln figure is a true work of art, a blending of ancient and modern crafts. Ten years of research and thousands of man hours by artists,

sculptors and skilled technicians—experts in the new field of Audio-Animatronics—went into the creation of this incredibly life-like representation of America's sixteenth president. The figure rises from a chair and addresses the Disneyland audience in the words of the Great Emancipator—words as applicable today as they were a century ago:

"Let us have faith that right makes might," counsels Lincoln, "and in that faith, let us, to the end, dare to do our duty as we understand it."

It is a presentation worthy of its name, ". . . a different and exciting way to stress history's importance to each of us," in the words of Walt Disney.

History of a vastly different sort, some of it predating man on earth, provided the themes for two of Disneyland's major additions in the $20 million expansion of 1966. One is the Primeval World. The photograph on the left will give you an idea of what it looks like!

Boarding trains of the Santa Fe & Disneyland Railroad, guests first travel through the Grand Canyon diorama, then are whisked back in time many millions of years to a day when giant creatures thundered over the land or soared like gliders across the sky. In the Primeval World, brontosaurus, stegosaurus, pterodactyl, triceratops and the frightening king of all the dinosaurs, tyrannosaurus, "come to life" through Audio-Animatronics.

These giant reptiles, ranging in height up to 15 feet, actually roamed the North American continent. In Disneyland, both the vegetarian brontosaurus and carnivorous tyrannosaurus, life-size and life-like, once more rule an earth changing from misty swampland to fiery, erupting volcanoes.

Historical fact and a dash of dashing fable also influenced Walt and his WED staff in the creation of New Orleans Square and its major adventure, the Pirates of the Caribbean.

165

In both atmosphere and architecture, New Orleans Square recreates the Crescent City in its golden age a century ago. Along its winding streets and in sheltered courtyards are Disneyland's most distinctive adventures in shopping and dining. Literally years of research and study went into the planning; out of this attention to detail and desire to recreate the classic traditions of old New Orleans came a series of "showcases." Here, in a land as large as Main Street, each shop and restaurant is one "act" in a thematic adventure; each dramatizes—in sight, in sound, in antique merchandise—one part of the exciting legend that was New Orleans, vintage 1850.

There is *Mlle. Antoinette's Parfumerie,* with mirrors that revive the lost art of painting in reverse; the decorations are painted first, and the mirrors are silvered only after the artist has completed his painstaking work. *The Creole Cafe* is distinguished by its tile floor and zinc-top coffee bar; espresso is served here from an ancient steam machine admired and purchased in Milan by Walt Disney. *Le Gourmet* offers hard-to-find culinary accessories, while the brick-walled *French Market* attracts diners with two tile murals depicting early New Orleans. And the exciting *Blue Bayou Restaurant* serves *poulet, crevettes, boeuf* and *poisson* by candlelight, which is only proper in a setting where moonlight shines all day long, Mardi Gras entertainment reigns, and the sight of the Bayou creates a mood at once mysterious and adventurous.

To find adventure of a totally different kind in New Orleans Square is to walk along Royal St., down Front St. into Pirate Alley. There, at the end of the quay, flat-bottom *bateaux* take on their seafaring guests, then glide serenely across the Blue Bayou Lagoon. Suddenly the boats plunge down a steep waterfall into the lair of the Pirates of the Caribbean.

"Avast there mates—ye that be young in heart! It's the gold of the New World we be searchin' for!" And you, vicarious visitor, are there, too— together with some of the wildest scoundrels who ever sailed the Spanish Main. A crew of dozens, all Audio-Animatronic, venture forth, cannons

167

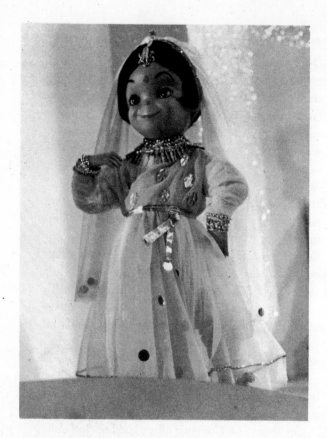

until the blare of trumpeting toy soldiers and a parade of toys from around the world announces each quarter hour.

In many ways, the happy spirit of It's A Small World expresses the *joie de vivre* of Disneyland and its chief architect. For even as these new adventures opened, Walt Disney was finalizing plans for additions just as ambitious. The major change: a new Tomorrowland.

Catalyst for this new area is American industry. Here the General Electric "Carousel of Progress," another World's Fair hit show, a new home; Monsanto welcomes guests on a trip into the micro-world of the atom; Douglas spirits earthmen on a flight to outer space; and the Bell System tours America in a new Circlevision production of "America the Beautiful."

But perhaps new Tomorrowland can best be placed in perspective through its "spaceport" and theme center, home base for four-passenger rocket ships that simulate the sensation of racing through distant space. Spiraling as high as an 18-story building, this towering structure is visible for miles—a gleaming metallic mountain—the biggest single structure ever built in Disneyland.

blazing and cutlasses drawn, to loot and plunder a port village.

On the other side of the Park, in Fantasyland, is another boat ride new to Disneyland in 1966. It's the happiest cruise that ever sailed 'round the globe: "It's a Small World."

Against stylized and colorful backgrounds of six continents, Audio-Animatronic children of more than 100 nations (all in colorful native costumes) sing and dance and weave the magic spell that charmed more than ten million people at the World's Fair. Toys and animals join the fun too; from the first chorus to the final fling, this is a merry fantasy of childhood expressed in the words of the title tune: "Though the mountains divide and the oceans are wide, it's a small world . . . after all!"

Disneyland's gaudiest marquee—the world's happiest clock, standing 30-feet high—calls visitors to It's A Small World. This wacky and whimsical clock actually *performs* the time, pulsating and vibrating and seemingly ready to explode . . .

What Is Not Yet Done

MORE than a century ago, the famous French author Alexis de Tocqueville heard the heartbeat of a new nation.

"America is a land of wonders," he wrote, "in which everything is in constant motion, and every change seems an improvement. No natural boundary seems to be set to the efforts of man; and in his eyes what is not yet done is only what he has not yet attempted to do."

What de Tocqueville wrote about America a hundred years ago could easily be said of Disneyland today. As Walt himself has said:

"I believe the fun is in building something, in bringing new things to life. We never do the same thing twice. After we've finished a job around here we head in another direction. We're always opening up new doors."

Sancho the Homing Steer

Down in West Texas, they still talk about longhorn cattle. The longhorns were quite a breed. They had weight. They had stamina. And they had horns that reached from here to Christmas. There are those who say that a longhorn was tough enough to stand off a wolf. A longhorn could stand off a man, too. That's why the breed has just about disappeared. They were too tough to handle.

Sancho was a longhorn—a very special longhorn. His story—what we know of it—began one summer day in 1903. It was a real Texas scorcher of a day—all dust devils and shimmering heat. A young rancher named Ed Kerr was riding along, minding his own business, when he looked up and saw buzzards circling. Ed knew that when buzzards were up, something had to be down. If it was a cow, he had a right to claim her unbranded calf. This was called mavericking, and it was an honest profession.

Ed checked out the nearest water hole. Sure enough, a longhorn cow had gotten herself stuck in the mud. She had departed this earth, leaving her calf an orphan.

Ed didn't lose any time. He slung that orphan calf over his horse. Then he got out of there, because there were other longhorns milling around in the brush. And longhorns reckon they can take care of their own better than any human.

Ed counted it a real lucky morning when he found that calf. He headed for his ranch, and the chores that were waiting.

As ranches go, Ed's place wasn't much. It was short on grass and short on water, but Ed had plans for drilling a deep well. Then he'd start building a real spread. Meantime, he was thankful for what he had.

Most of all, Ed was thankful for his pretty Mexican wife, Maria. And Maria was something to be thankful for. She loved everything. She loved the little two-room house Ed had built for her. She loved the chickens and the turkeys and the ducks that pecked in the yard, and the goat that ran to her when she opened the door. She loved the geese who thought they owned the water trough. Most of all, she loved Ed.

And when Ed showed up with that muddy, forlorn little calf slung across his horse, Maria just naturally loved the calf, too.

"I'll call him Sancho," she announced. "It means 'pet', you know."

Ed looked around the ranch yard at the chickens and turkeys and geese. He looked at the goat and her kid, and even at Rassler, the friendly mongrel who was supposed to be a watchdog. "Pet?" said Ed. "You've got a yard full of pets now!"

Maria didn't deny it. But the little calf would be the number one Sancho, said she.

So the calf got a name and a home and someone to look after him, and he liked that fine. He rewarded Maria for her care. He ate everything she gave him, and quite a few things that she never thought of giving him.

All longhorns like to pick a special place for their own. Sancho was no different. His special place was under the mesquite tree that grew in the ranch yard. Maria called it his *querencia* —his homing place.

Some of Sancho's neighbors didn't like the way the longhorn claimed the mesquite tree. The geese hissed at him. The rooster flew at him. But Sancho was bigger than any of them. He always won the argument—unless he tackled the geese on their home ground, which was the watering

trough. Then he'd get a nasty nip for his trouble, and he'd run to Maria for sympathy.

The sympathy was always forthcoming. Sometimes Maria fed Sancho hot peppers from her bowl. Sometimes she gave him an enchilada or a tamale. Best of all, Sancho loved the tortillas that Maria made, patting the corn dough into thin, thin cakes with her hands.

Sancho was one of the family. He had the run of the ranch, except for one precious half acre. That was Maria's corn field.

Often Sancho stood at the brush fence that surrounded the corn field and stared at the pretty green shoots that were just beyond his reach. They were tempting. But the moment the steer tried to get into the field, Rassler the dog would come barking and snapping at his heels. That would bring Maria running with her broom. Sancho would retreat to his *querencia* to brood about the unlovable qualities of dogs—especially dogs like Rassler.

You see, Maria had great hopes for the corn field. Ed believed in cattle, but Maria believed in the good earth. She figured she would grow a fine crop of corn, sell it and buy a mule. Then she would grow even bigger crops of corn. So no one, not even Sancho, could interfere with the corn field.

The seasons passed and the corn grew tall and sweet. Sancho grew, too. He grew until he was half a ton of fine, tortilla-fed beef. And everyone on the Kerr ranch was happy, except possibly Ed.

To Ed, Sancho was trouble on the hoof. He ate too much. And on a ranch where water was always a problem, he used up much more than he was worth.

"He drinks like a herd of buffalo," said Ed to Maria one evening. They were sitting on a bench in the yard, enjoying whatever cool breezes happened along. "We got so darned little water as it is, the ducks forgot how to swim."

Maria knew this was true. She murmured something about the poor little ducks. She murmured something else about perhaps getting rid of Sancho. But not now. *Mañana.* Tomorrow. Later.

Ed sighed. He knew there would be no getting rid of Sancho. The steer was Maria's special pet.

Just then, Sancho got into his first big trouble. He came to the house looking for a bedtime snack. Something tasty—some corn, perhaps.

Sancho put his head in at the window. There was corn there, all right. Several ears hung from the rafters. The trouble was, Sancho couldn't get to it from where he was. Sancho moseyed around the house, well out of sight of Ed and Maria, until he found an open door. It was an outright invitation to a hungry steer. Sancho moved into the house and reached for the corn.

It was still out of his reach. The steer gave an angry bellow, backed off, upset the table and tried a clumsy leap at the corn.

Ed heard the bellow and the crash and headed for the kitchen at a run. He wasn't quick enough. Before he could get inside, Sancho had made several more lunges at the luscious corn. He had upset the cupboard, sending pans and dishes flying. Worst of all, he had knocked down Ed's rifle. It went off with a roar that frightened Sancho half out of his mind.

What happened next was also unpleasant. Ed grabbed an iron skillet that happened to be handy and swung it at the steer. It caught Sancho squarely on the rump. Sancho got out of there, taking the kitchen door down as he went.

Ed came boiling out of the house, waving the skillet. "I'm going to bust him wide open!" he roared.

But Maria didn't see it that way. She grabbed Ed's arm and said that Sancho was just a poor dumb brute who couldn't tell them what he wanted. "You have taught him his lesson," she said. "Come and help me. We will fix it, and everything will be the same."

Ed grumbled and raged, but he gave in. In time the table was mended, the cupboard was put back to rights, and things at the ranch went on as before.

Then Sancho committed an unforgivable sin.

Maria was busy that day, and Ed was out on the range. Even Rassler was off on some doggy expedition. So there was no one to stop Sancho when he decided he would move into paradise. And paradise, to Sancho, was Maria's corn field.

A brush fence is no problem to a longhorn. With no Rassler to snap at his heels, Sancho was through the fence and nibbling away in no time.

It was delicious!

Sancho ate and ate and ate. The more he ate, the happier he felt—until Ed rode into the ranch yard. And close behind Ed came Rassler the dog.

There was a shouting and a scrambling, and Ed grabbed his lasso. Maria came running with her skillet—that very same skillet that had seriously damaged Sancho's pride once before.

Rassler charged with every hair bristling and every tooth bared, and Sancho took off. Of course he trampled the corn as he went.

"My corn!" cried Maria.

Rassler barked even louder, and Ed's lasso flew through the air and settled over Sancho's long horns. But once he had lassoed Sancho, Ed had no way of stopping him. Sancho dragged the rancher the entire length of the corn field. Then, at the far end of the field, the steer turned and headed in a new direction.

"You bad one!" shouted Maria. "You're ruining my corn!"

Ed suddenly got tired of being dragged, and let go of the rope. Sancho made straight for the mesquite tree, the rope still trailing from his horns.

Maria began to cry. There was hardly enough left of her corn crop to make one decent tortilla, let alone buy a mule.

Ed got slowly to his feet. "Maria," he said, and

his voice shook with anger, "this ranch ain't big enough for us and that steer, too. He's got to go."

This time, Maria did not argue.

But if Maria was ready to sell Sancho, who would buy him? The country was already cattle poor. Then, like a fresh breeze out of the north, word came that there was a government order for seven thousand head of beef to be delivered to Montana.

It meant a new life for West Texas. It meant prosperity. The local ranchers picked out a holding ground and began to bring in their cattle. In a few days, the trail herd was shaping up.

The boss for the cattle drive was a man named Shiner. He signed Ed on for the drive. Maria's heart was heavy, for it meant that Ed would be gone for almost a year. But the wages were good, and they needed the money. Maria would have to run the ranch by herself. She could do it, she knew. So there was only one decision she had to make. She made it when Mr. Shiner rode by the day before the cattle drive began. She sold Sancho.

Shiner was glad to get the steer. Sancho was tame; he would be a good lead steer. He could set the pace and the rest of the herd would follow him.

Maria was to get beef price plus ten dollars for Sancho. She asked only one more thing. She wanted Shiner to take Sancho away immediately —before she could change her mind.

Sancho didn't like it and put up a stiff argument. But Shiner and Ed had all the answers, and they had ropes. It was adios to Sancho's *querencia* and to Maria.

The next day they gave Sancho a bell and put him at the head of the herd, and they started him walking. And every time he tried to slip away from the herd and head home to Maria, one of the outriders would be after him and he'd wind up back at the head of that herd.

By the second day, Sancho began to take things in stride. He began acting as if he'd been a lead steer all his life. He moved out, and the herd moved behind him. It was the beginning of the longest trail drive ever—fifteen hundred miles.

Ten days out and a hundred miles from home,

they crossed into New Mexico. They followed the Pecos River for a while, then cut across the desert to climb to Raton Pass. Two and a half months out of Texas, they moved into Wyoming. Then they followed the grass into Nebraska and South Dakota.

The trouble was, Sancho didn't care that much for grass. It would do all right when nothing better was around. But by this time, Sancho had discovered the cook wagon. To him, the sour dough for the biscuits smelled mighty like Maria's tortillas. More than once, Cooky had had to drive that crazy lead steer away. The men thought this was pretty funny, until the morning in the Black Hills when they were just getting the horses saddled up.

No one was paying any attention to Sancho, and the steer didn't see any good reason why he shouldn't have a little snack before they hit the trail again. He trotted up to the back of the cook

wagon and put his big, greedy nose into the bucket of sour dough starter. And, once having gotten himself into the dough, Sancho couldn't get himself out of the sticky stuff.

Sancho couldn't bellow with that bucket on his nose, so he banged the bucket against the side of the wagon.

Sancho couldn't be expected to know that good range horses are always jittery, especially in the cool of the morning. That's when they'll spook at the sound of a cactus dropping a needle. And Sancho was making a lot more noise than a cactus. He was making enough uproar to light the fuse on those horses as if they were fifty kegs of dynamite.

The next thing the men knew, the horses had broken through the rope of their make-shift corral and were out and running. And since there are few things more catching than a stampede, the cattle ran, too.

It took two days to get the herd back together again. The cost was two hundred cows and fourteen horses.

Sancho had never been more unpopular.

Then a pair of Indians showed up and demanded payment for trailing the herd across their land. Shiner was willing to pay. He didn't want any trouble with the Indians, and he didn't want any more trouble with a nutty lead steer. He gave them Sancho.

In a way, Ed hated to see Sancho go. He knew that, to the Indians, the longhorn was just beef on the hoof. But Shiner was boss, and he owned Sancho now.

Just the same, Ed followed along when the Indians took the steer. They had some trouble getting him to go their way, but in the end they managed. Their camp wasn't much of a place. Ed was watching from a distance, and he counted three tepees and eight braves, including the one who was sharpening a knife.

There was a dog, too. As Ed watched, the dog moved in and started to snap at Sancho's heels.

Sancho just hated dogs, and this one was too much like Rassler to suit him. The steer began to kick and buck and sidle, and no matter how those Indians tried, they couldn't hold him.

It didn't take Sancho long. After all, he was an expert at creating stampedes. In no time at all he had run off the Indian's horses, knocked down two tepees and was headed for the tall timber, as free as the day he was born.

Ed grinned and rode back to join Shiner. He wasn't going to worry about Sancho. That steer could take care of himself.

But Sancho didn't want to take care of himself. He wanted his *querencia*. He wanted Maria. He wanted to go back to Texas, and no matter that it was more than twelve hundred miles away.

Sancho started walking.

What happened after that, no one knows for sure. One rancher told of seeing a lone longhorn headed south across a corner of Nebraska. He was going steadily and with determination. And in the dead of winter, a longhorn steer appeared in a little town in the San Juan Mountains of New Mexico. The townsfolk talked of it long afterward. Who ever heard of a tame longhorn? There had never been a longhorn so tame that it let itself be harnessed to a child's sled. But that's what this steer had done. Then, before it could be corraled, it had just walked on.

It must have been that way for Sancho. It must have been days and weeks and months of just

177

walking. No doubt there were times when he drifted astray, but somehow he always kept moving south, led by memories and a strange homing instinct.

By the time spring came, Sancho was almost home. He was picking his way through the Sierra Diablo Mountains when he met the mountain lions. It wasn't an important meeting, for Sancho was long past being afraid of a couple of overgrown cats. And the lions knew that the best view of a longhorn was when he was leaving. They kept clear of Sancho.

Then they caught the scent of something really toothsome. They caught the scent of a horse.

Now this particular horse was bringing a homesick cowboy all the way from Montana to Texas. It was Ed Kerr's horse, and it had been staked out the night before when Ed bedded down. Ed planned an early start, so he could be home by noon.

The lions didn't get the horse. They tried. They tried awfully hard. And they scared him so that he pulled up his stake and ran.

Ed was awake in an instant. The sun was just up, and he got in one good shot that dropped the female cat. Then the male faded back behind some rocks, and Ed started up the hill. He wanted to get that second killer. But before he went far, his foot twisted on the loose shale and he went down. He rolled and slid for a few feet, then lay still.

They say that a mountain lion won't tackle a man—at least not often. But just once is once too many. This cat sensed that his mate was dead, and that the man lying so still had had something to do with it. Moving as smoothly as tawny velvet, he came toward Ed.

Now Sancho hadn't done all that walking just to be a hero. But Sancho hated cats, and when he came around the shoulder of the hill and saw the cougar standing over Ed, he charged. At first the cat thought he might stay and fight it out, and tried to strike at Sancho's lowered horns. But then he leaped over Ed and disappeared up into the rocks.

Sancho was right pleased when he saw he'd found an old friend. And when Ed came to his senses and sat up, shaking his head to clear away the mists, the feeling was mutual.

Soon Ed and Sancho had things arranged between them. Since Ed's horse was gone heaven knows where, and since Sancho was going in Ed's direction anyway, Ed slung a saddle on the steer and Sancho started to walk again.

Maria was in her corn field when Ed came riding up on Sancho. When she saw Ed, she got much too busy hugging and kissing him to ask questions. And by the time she did get to the questions, Sancho had settled himself comfortably under the mesquite tree. It was Ed himself who fed the homing steer a fine dinner of tortillas.

So, at the end of the trail, everything turned out fine for everybody. Ed used his money from the drive to drill the well he'd always wanted. Maria kept raising her corn, but instead of a mule to help with the plowing, she used Sancho. She thought everyone on the ranch should pull his own weight.

Sancho didn't mind a bit, because every evening, under his mesquite tree, he found a time of peace—and a heap of tortillas.

A male black trunk fish—the females are black with white spots.

Fishes of the Indian & Pacific Oceans

The Indian and Pacific Oceans support a far richer fauna than is found in the tropical Atlantic Ocean. The largest concentrations of species are again found on the coral reefs, and the following figures give some indication of their enormous variety. Over 900 species inhabit the coastal reefs off Ceylon, over 1200 species are found off the eastern coast of Africa, and over 2000 off the Philippines. Not all of these species are coral fish of course—some are irregular visitors to the reefs—but the reefs remain the centers of all this teeming life.

The numerous fishes inhabiting a coral reef vary considerably in appearance and habits and the different conditions found in different parts of the reef attract markedly different populations. The main division is between the fishes of the land side and the sea side of the reef.

On the sea side we find the strong swimmers, for naturally this side is subject to the influence of surf, strong currents and the ebb and flow of tides. The fish living on this side must be able to cope with these rough water conditions. It is interesting that we find many small species such as anthiids and damsel fish on this side, as well as the larger species such as the red-toothed trigger fish, the imperial angel fish, the fusilier fishes and the sea basses. The cleaning wrasse also occurs most frequently on the steep side of the reef.

In the calmer waters inside the reef we find the numerous species that prefer this zone because they are weak swimmers or because they need the protection of a finer tracery of coral than grows on the outer side of the reef. (This points to a basic rule: not only the more varied the sea conditions are, but the more varied the structure of the substratum is, the more varied the fishes will be.) In a typical inner reef community we find the weak-swimming sunfishes and trunk fishes, also surgeon fishes, anemone fishes, many species of damsel fish, morays, wrasses, etc.

Differences of population also occur at different depths. Most anemone fish, damsel fish, wrasses and surgeon fish live in the shallows. The butterfly fish, snappers, ribbon fish, and small anthiids of the outer reef prefer the deeper layers. Soldier, or squirrel, fish and cardinal fish live in fairly deep layers, hiding in large holes on the steep side of the reef by day and emerging to search for food when darkness falls. Most of the deep water fish are red, which is a protective color in dark waters, and a few of them have very large eyes, an example of adaptation to the darkness.

On the flat strips of sand connecting the reef and the beach we find the homes of other species such as the flat fishes, rays and goat fishes. The goat fishes have two long movable whiskers hanging downwards in front of their mouths. These serve as feelers, scanning the sea floor beneath the fish as it swims along in search of prey. Where the sand strips are weed-grown, large populations of gobies and blennies occur. Isolated coral formations on the sands attract small colonies of the three-striped damsel fish.

Young damsel fish live in groups of about a dozen in a large piece of coral. As they mature they separate into pairs and a large piece of coral may house several pairs. The damsel fish are deeply attached to their homes and if a piece of coral in which they live is dislodged they will return to it, even if it has drifted several meters away.

Damsel fish are popular aquarium fishes and the fishermen of the coral reef catch them easily by simply picking up their coral home and transferring it underwater into a plastic bag. In this way they catch dozens at a time. For this method to be successful, however, there must be no other hiding place close at hand, for if there is the fish will leave their home to seek refuge. But if there is no other shelter the fish will remain in the piece of coral even if it is twisted off and brought to the surface.

One of the most beautiful fishes to be found on the sands along and between the reefs is the flying gurnard. The tremendously enlarged pectoral fins of this fish are used for long glides over

The clown zebra fish feeds by taking mouthfuls of sand or mud from the sea floor and sifting out the edible material. For this reason it is difficult to keep in captivity.

the sands. It has been suggested that these gurnards are also able to propel themselves out of the water, like flying fish, but this seems to be a matter of great doubt and has yet to be proved conclusively. Although the flying gurnards are similar to the other species of gurnards in many ways, there is a big difference in the build of their skulls and they do, in fact, belong to a separate order.

Cleaning services are performed by some fishes in the tropical Atlantic Ocean, and this phenomenon also occurs in the Red Sea and the Indian and Pacific Oceans. However, it is a remarkable fact that in these waters the number of different species performing this service is far smaller. This may be because they can easily cope with the demand for their services and there is therefore no need for other species to specialize this way.

In this large oceanic region only a few species of the genus *Labroides* make the cleaning of other fish their lifework. The cleaning wrasse is be-

lieved to feed entirely on what it nibbles from the skin of other fishes. Observers who have watched this fish in its own environment for a long time report that it does not look for any other food. A second species of wrasse, the yellow four-stripe wrasse which lives in the Red Sea, only occasionally cleans other fish.

Young cleaning wrasses live in small groups on the coral reefs. At a later stage of life each chooses a mate and the couple live in holes in a definite place, usually a distinctive part of the coral reef, called a cleaning station. They swim over their homes in a very characteristic way, dancing up and down, keeping their heads in almost the same place and swaying their blue and white tails. At the approach of a client, a predatory fish in particular, the movement quickens and it is believed that this 'inviting dance' is the result of two contradictory movements of approach and flight. The cleaning fish wants to swim up to work on the predator but at the

The moray lives in holes and chasms of rocky coasts and coral reefs. It feeds mainly on octopuses but is also partial to crabs and fish. It is rather an aggressive animal.

The horsehead fish, a bizarre creature of the coral reef, has sharp spines.

A zebra moray. Its conspicuous markings make it easily identifiable.

same time it is afraid and has an equally strong urge to flee. The other fishes on the reef know the cleaning stations and visit them from time to time. When a fish wants to be cleaned it signals to the wrasses by its attitude, usually by tilting its head up or down and stretching its fins. It hovers over the station, keeping afloat with very slight movements of its pectoral fins. The wrasse then swims up and starts cleaning immediately, usually beginning at the customer's head and working gradually along to its tail.

The cleaning wrasses search the customer's skin for parasites, crustaceans in particular. (In captivity they leave parasitic ciliates alone.) If the customer has wounds, the edges are nibbled clean and dead tissue is removed, but when the cleaner's activities irritate the customer the latter will shake its body vigorously, sometimes even taking revenge by chasing the cleaner. Large fishes open their mouths and gill-covers wide during cleaning and upon this sign the cleaners swim in fearlessly to pick out particles of food from between the teeth and gills. Cleaners sometimes signal to the customer to open its mouth by nudging it.

During cleaning a customer may keep so still that it gradually sinks down to the coral, and many fishes turn pale. This has led some observers to believe that they do so to show up the parasites to the cleaner, which is an attractive but unproven explanation of such behavior. When a customer wants the cleaner to stop, it almost closes its mouth and then opens it again quickly, shaking its body once or twice. The cleaner then leaves its host immediately and swims back to its station to await another customer.

Clients come and go at the cleaning stations and will often queue up to await their turn. Schools of fish also visit the cleaners regularly. Part of the school hovers above the station for cleaning while the rest swim around until the cleaners have finished their job. Then the whole school may swim away or the cleaned ones may swim around and wait while the others are cleaned. The American biologists, Limbaugh and Pederson, once watched a single cleaning fish deal with over three hundred customers in six hours!

The cleaners obviously have an important function in the reef community and their indispensability was confirmed by Limbaugh, who experimented by removing all the known cleaners from two reefs near the Bahamas. The results were spectacular. Within two weeks many fishes had left the reefs to search for other cleaning stations; the remaining population showed all kinds of damage to skin and fins and suffered from open wounds and fungi diseases. Their condition only improved when young wrasses grew up to replace those that had been removed.

The fish that accept the services of cleaners belong to widely different families: sea basses, butterfly fishes, angel fishes, turkey fishes, surgeon fishes, morays, wrasses, file fishes, horse mackerel (which swim in from the open sea in search of cleaning fish), trigger fishes and even giant rays. The cleaners also clean each other, mates cleaning their partners at a later stage of life.

Beside the cleaners of the genus *Labroides*, there are various species that only clean occasionally. Young angel fishes in particular are known for this activity and they are also found in the Red Sea, Indian and Pacific Oceans. Young pennant coral fishes also clean occasionally.

The fact that cleaning symbiosis is a long-established feature of reef life is proved by the emergence of a species of false cleaner. This fish, called the 'bogus cleaner', closely resembles the cleaning wrasses in appearance and imitates their behavior for its own ends. It is such a perfect imitation that dealers occasionally sell it for a cleaning wrasse.

Dealers and keepers of aquariums may be deceived but the reef fishes have to learn by bitter experience, for the bogus cleaner eats their scales and skin. It behaves like a cleaning wrasse, inviting others from a distinctive place on the reef, but when an unsuspecting fish swims up to be cleaned the bogus cleaner attacks in a flash, savagely biting pieces from the fish's skin or fins. It is not known whether fish that have been attacked in this way somehow learn to recognize and avoid the bogus cleaners or whether thereafter they avoid the cleaning stations altogether.

Two pairs of striped damsel fish swimming among the branches of their coral home. If danger approaches they dive deep into its center.

The giant sea bass may reach a length of 10 feet. This is a young bass; the adults are almost totally black.

At all events the bogus cleaners must be fairly rare members of the reef community, or the real cleaners would be thrown out of business.

In 1961 the German animal psychologist, Eibl-Eibesfeldt, discovered and described a cleaning relationship between a fish and a sea urchin in the waters around the Nicobar Islands in the Bay of Bengal. He found that small cardinal fish nibble unwanted matter from the skins of the urchins, which even fold down their spines to bare the skin for their cleaners. During the day the cardinal fish move busily from one sea urchin to another but they leave their hosts during the night.

Such an association between cardinal fish and sea urchins has also been discovered on the Great Barrier Reef of Australia and in the Red Sea, although it is not yet known whether the cardinal fish in these areas clean the skins of their hosts.

The cleaning symbiosis may develop between these species when the fish learns to appreciate the sea urchin as a safe hiding place—or it may not develop at all. We cannot assume from Ebil-Eibesfeldt's findings in the Nicobar Islands that all cardinal fish everywhere clean the sea urchins they shelter among. Nor can we assume that the other fishes using sea urchins as hiding places

perform a similar service. Further research may bring other factors to light.

The sea urchin certainly has other guests. We may see certain species of tropical cling fishes, or the peculiar razor fish, hiding between the spines. The color pattern of these fishes is well adapted to life, or just occasional hiding, between the spines: the cling fishes are dark blue or almost black with a few bright white bands, and the razor fish is pale with three dark brown stripes running from nose to tail, one on each side and one on its back. The color pattern makes them invisible in the mass of spines, among which they hide in a vertical position.

The cling fish hold on to the spines with their suckers, either head downwards or tail downwards. They do not clean the urchin of parasites: instead they nibble its feet (found between the spines all over its body). They must eat other food as well, otherwise the urchin would not survive, even though it can grow new feet quite quickly.

The razor fish have no sucker to help them to keep upright among the spines: they do not need one. Their natural position, both when resting and swimming, is vertical—heads down and tails up.

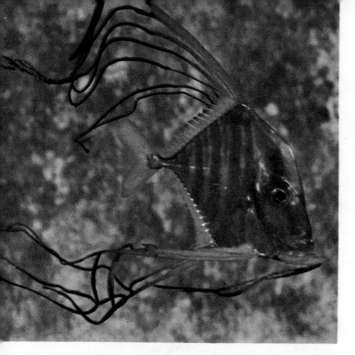

In maturity the fringe fish loses the trailing steamers attached to its fin rays.

The razor fish is a very strange creature. It has an extremely compressed body whose ventral side is razor sharp. (It is so like a blade that the natives of the Pacific islands sometimes use a dried razor fish for peeling fruit. The dried razor fish is stiff enough to use for this purpose because its body is enclosed in an armor of hard transparent plates.)

Although the razor fish's body is too slender to hold much food, this animal spends most of the day hunting and feeding. This is because its mouth, at the end of its long hard snout, is so small that it cannot eat anything but the tiniest planktonic organisms, one by one.

The razor fish is a master swimmer, despite its peculiar swimming position. After hovering head downwards for several moments it shoots backwards through the water. Speeding up, it may assume a more horizontal position, and when racing at top speed to escape an enemy it becomes completely horizontal, swimming in the same fashion as any other fish.

The shoaling habit is strong in razor fish. Dozens of them will swim together around the coral reefs, keeping in close formation except when hunting for food. Even when they are hunting, the members of the group keep roughly together, displaying an amazing number of movements: quick turns, pirouettes, sudden bursts of speed up, down, backwards and forwards, all performed with the greatest of precision and ease.

For many years experts were uncertain as to which way up the razor fish normally swam. Some said its normal position was head downwards and others disagreed. It was only in recent years that observers watching the fish in its natural habitat realized why they had previously been misled: the razor fish normally swims with its head facing the substratum. In its natural habitat, this means that it swims head downwards, facing the sea floor, but sometimes aquarium specimens swim with their heads upwards, searching the walls and roof of their tank for food.

The razor fish undergoes as drastic a metamorphosis between youth and maturity as the flat fish. The young razor fishes are formed in the same way as any other fish and they swim horizontally. As they develop, however, the vertebral column begins to bend downwards at the head end, forcing the two dorsal fins towards the tail. By the time the fish is approximately an inch long, both the tail fin and the second dorsal fin have moved around to the ventral side of the body. The first dorsal fin becomes a sharp spine at the 'tail' end of the body and the fish swims in its adult position, head downwards.

Another surprising relationship between reef animals is that of the cardinal fish and the conch, a species of mollusk. Cardinal fishes do not appear to perform any service for the conch, but they make their home within the shelter of its mantle, only leaving it at night when they hunt for food.

A much closer association has been observed between shrimps and gobies. The shrimp takes a great deal of trouble building a burrow in the sand for the goby and its mate to live in. It then works day and night to keep the burrow in good repair, while the gobies stand guard at the entrance. As soon as danger appears, the gobies dive into the burrow, thus warning the shrimp. The 'watchmen' are very useful to the shrimp which cannot see very well and might not otherwise escape in time. The shrimp also eats food brought home by the gobies.

Such associations between burrowing crustaceans and gobies have been seen in several parts of the Red Sea and the Indian Ocean. Off the coast of California an even more remarkable relationship has been discovered. This is between a shrimp and a *blind* goby! Here the shrimp appears to gain nothing. The blind goby is completely dependent upon it for its home and food and will die when the shrimp dies unless another comes along to look after it.

Off the western coast of North America there is a species of goby which has an entirely different relationship with a shrimp or crab. The goby and the crab or shrimp live together, often in a worm's burrow. When the goby catches a prey that is too big or too hard to eat, it brings it home and presents it to the crab for breaking up. The crab tears it apart with its strong pincers and as soon as this is done the goby snatches up the pieces and departs to eat them, leaving several tidbits behind as a fee for the crab's service. If the goby lives alone in its burrow it will trap a passing crab into performing this service.

The magnificent red bass. Unlike most basses, this species is very shy,
hiding by day and feeding by night (when its red color appears black).

Ribbon fish live together in large shoals on the coral reefs. This picture shows how well protective color patterns mask their shape.

One of the strangest relationships among marine animals is the intimacy between several species of tiny coral fish and certain very large sea anemones. Sea anemones, including the species adopted by these fishes, have numerous stinging cells on their tentacles, and the stinging cells shoot out and inject poison into anything that touches their triggers. Normally one shot of this poison is enough to kill or paralyse any small animal that receives it. The victim is then devoured by the sea anemone. Even human beings experience severe pain after being stung by certain anemones. But the small coral fishes we are about to describe do not seem to be affected —they actually choose to live among the dangerous tentacles.

In the Red Sea and the Indian and Pacific Oceans there are enormous sea anemones with diameters of three feet or more. Yet among their forests of tentacles we see brightly colored fishes behaving as if the dangerous anemone made the safest and loveliest home on earth. They dart in and out without being hurt and even rub themselves against the tentacles as if they were snuggling down in a bed of feathers. While there are certain species of anemone that do not have stinging cells, or at least possess only a few, the anemones adopted as homes by the anemone fishes all have highly toxic tentacles.

What is the secret of the anemone fishes' immunity? Why should anemones that sting and eat all other small fish allow these particular fishes to move freely among their tentacles? This is a mystery which has intrigued biologists for many years and the answer is still not known, although there are many explanations.

188

The first idea was that the anemones must belong to a non-stinging type. This was quickly and easily disproved. Investigation of the tentacles showed that the anemones had batteries of very potent stinging cells.

Then it was suggested that the anemone fishes made themselves known to the anemones by some form of distinctive behavior and were then accepted by them. This idea was also dropped, firstly because the behavioral pattern of the anemones was unlikely to develop along such lines, and secondly because the apparently distinctive movements of the anemone fishes under observation were found to be directly due to the captivity in observation tanks. (Captive

The black and white striped sea bass—when in danger, it secretes a poisonous substance.

anemone fishes, with a few exceptions, swim up and down in one place and this movement was thought to be attractive to sea anemones, causing a welcome current of water to flow over them. However, it is now understood to be a movement of frustrated flight: the fish wants to escape from its unnatural enclosure but cannot. Anemone fishes never behave in this way in their natural environment.) Finally, experiments showed that the anemone would not sting an anemone fish that kept still.

Current research may be coming nearer to the correct explanation. Observers have noted that an anemone fish whose skin is damaged will not approach an anemone. When, in an experiment, damaged anemone fishes were forced to swim among the anemone's tentacles they were instantly stung and eaten. This pointed to the fact that the skin of the healthy anemone fish played a significant part in its immunity.

Further experiments were made with a piece of sponge. This was impregnated with the mucous secretion from the skin of a healthy anemone fish and moved along the anemone's tentacles: no reaction occurred from the anemone. Then a plain piece of sponge was moved among its tentacles: it was immediately stung and eaten.

Stinging cells that have been removed from the tentacles and brought into contact with the skin secretion of anemone fishes do not react, but they lash out as soon as they are touched with the secretion of other fishes.

The snapper belongs to a large family that has many representatives in the tropic seas.

189

The eggs of a clown anemone fish at a late stage of development, when the fish inside are visible.

A pair of anemone fish hover above their large anemone home in the Red Sea.

All of these findings lead us to suppose that it is a chemical substance produced by the skin of healthy anemone fishes that gives them their immunity to the anemone's stinging cells.

Several questions remain. For example, is the chemical substance always present in sufficient quantity to protect the fish, or is it the result of a chemical reaction occurring when the fish touches the tentacles? This question was first raised when scientists saw that anemone fishes that had been kept away from their host for a long time did not immediately swim around the tentacles when they were brought back.

Most anemone fishes approach their host with caution at first and seem extremely reluctant to touch the tentacles. They swim up to the anemone in the end but the first contact is very short and the fish seems to receive a slight sting. Gradually it becomes less guarded, touching the anemone bravely and receiving no sting.

This behavior seems to indicate that the chemical substance is only made, or made in sufficient quantities, after the fish has been in contact with the anemone. But it still does not help to explain why sea anemones of different species do not welcome all anemone fishes. The clown anemone fish never lives with *Radianthus knekenthali* and will also be stung by an anemone that houses the black anemone fish.

All anemone fishes belong to the genus *Amphiprion* and spend their life in and around the anemones. Their larvae live in the upper water layers and feed on plankton until they have grown larger. They then move down to the bottom and find an anemone for themselves, inhabiting the forests of tentacles in large schools. As they grow older the anemone fishes push each other out until one adult pair remains in sole possession. The mates then fiercely defend their territory, making some noise in doing so. They make a threatening noise when an intruder is still some distance away from the anemone and the noise changes in tone when they start to fight. When an anemone fish is attacked by one of its kind and does not want to fight, or for some reason cannot fight, it makes a special noise to let the other know, moving its head sideways while doing so.

The anemone fish's chief source of food is plankton but it will not go far from its nest when searching for it. At the slightest warning of danger it darts back to the anemone's shelter. During the night the anemone fish lies on its side between the anemone tentacles, which may even fold over it. At spawning time the fish cleans an area at the base of the anemone to deposit its eggs, safe under the shield of tentacles. The parents guard the eggs and take turns to wave their pectoral fins around the eggs to keep them clean. They also take the eggs into their mouths now and again for cleaning. The young anemone fish hatch in about eight days, helped on by the parents who take the eggs into their mouths more frequently during the night of hatching.

A symbiotic relationship also exists between sea anemones and spotted damsel fish. Dozens of young damsel fish may live in a large sea anemone but they seem to lose their immunity to its stinging cells with adulthood. One of the Mediterranean gobies, *Gobius bucchichi,* has also been seen living with an anemone (*Anemonia sulcata*).

A coral reef has many other inhabitants and, watching the shallow waters on the coastal side, we may see large schools of young striped catfish. They swim in orderly rows, scanning the sands for food with their barbels. Their behavior at the approach of danger is spectacular: in an instant all the fishes mass together to form a ball, their tails toward the center and their heads pointing outwards. The ball looks like a porcupine bowling along the sands and predators do not know what to make of it, with the result that they leave it alone. This behavior of a group of individuals suddenly transforming themselves into a compact mass may be compared with the behavior of starlings, which assume a cluster formation as soon as a predatory bird comes near.

Wrasses react to danger in a totally different manner, diving into the sands at incredibly high speed. They also take to the shelter of the sand at night time—and the knowledge of day and night seems instinctive in them. When kept in

Anemone fish lay their eggs at the base of their anemone and take turns to guard them.

tanks for observation they still disappear in the sand at night, even if a light above the tank is kept burning all night long.

With the wrasses we come again to a phenomenon that occurs very frequently among coral fishes: the color pattern of youth is totally different from the pattern of adulthood. The rainbow fish is a good example. The young differ so much in pattern and color from the adults that they were at first classified as a different species. The same mistake was made with the young of the ringed angel fish and the imperial angel fish.

A large number of species seem to aim at inconspicuous behavior. Hiding from enemies is a good reason, but many inhabitants also try to be invisible to their prey. The stone fishes are masters of the art. They look exactly like underwater rocks or stones thickly overgrown with algae, and this has earned them their name. An unsuspecting animal that comes near to the patiently waiting stone fish may suddenly find itself disappearing into the stone fish's enormous mouth.

The stone fish is also very dangerous to man because it has large, bulbous poison glands at the base of its dorsal spines. If a fisherman accidentally steps on a hidden stone fish the spines will penetrate into his foot, even through the sole of a shoe, and the poison will enter the wound. The poison is of a highly dangerous kind and may even cause death.

Scorpion fishes, such as the humpback, hide between stones and corals for the same purpose. Their bright colors cannot be seen between stones overgrown with red and yellow sponges and algae. Another scorpion fish, sometimes called the Napoleon fish, also tries to remain unseen. It seldom swims but uses its large pectoral fins to 'walk' over the corals in search of food. Scorpion fishes have another pecularity: they shed their skins from time to time. They do not sit still at the approach of danger but put their trust in their protective coloring and sway slowly as if they were inanimate and moved by a water current. One species, *Taenionotus triacanthus*, is called 'swinging fish' in Holland.

The angler fishes are equally skilled in the art of disguise and deception. There are many species in this family (*Antennaridae*) and all are provided with the same ingenious method of catching their prey. The first ray of the dorsal fin is movable as a separate organ and threaded at the top with a bundle of long and short whiskers. This fishing rod is waved back and forth at the approach of a prey and the lure looks exactly like a group of small worms. This entices the victim which, as soon as it is near enough to the

An imperial angel fish looking out from its coral cave in the Red Sea.

angler's enormous mouth, is gobbled up. The anglers, sometimes called frogfishes, are gluttons and gulp up prey much larger than themselves which, happily, their elastic stomachs are able to accommodate.

Scorpion fish are not easily seen, but turkey fishes of the genus *Pterois* are striking, even flamboyant, in appearance. Their large pectoral fins with long protruding rays add to their impact. Turkey fish hunt at twilight, when they are less conspicuous. They use their pectoral fins to corner their prey, driving the victim into a confined space from which it cannot escape and is soon snapped up. The spines on the dorsal fins of the turkey fish are poisonous and may give a fisherman a very painful puncture wound, possibly causing paralysis. These spines are not used as weapons of attack, but when attacked by other predators, the turkey fish defends itself by turning the raised spines toward the attacker and waiting. Turkey fishes are not aggressive animals.

The bogus puffer is an example of a totally different kind of protection. In appearance it is an almost perfect imitation of the poisonous puffer but it is in fact quite harmless. To add to credibility, it usually joins small shoals of poisonous puffers and in this way escapes attack by predators.

Numerous species of coral fish, such as the butterfly fishes, have extended snouts for picking

The humpback scorpion fish lies camouflaged on the algae-covered stones of the reef floor.

The stone fish, equally indistinguishable from its background, has extremely sharp and poisonous dorsal spines.

out food from small crevices in the corals. A few other examples are the pincet fish, the birdfish, and the twinspot wrasse. The file fishes are similarly adapted. *Pervagor Melanocephalus*, for example, has a fairly pointed snout that enables it to extract tube worms from their tubes and small crustaceans from their hiding places between the corals. *Oxymonacanthus longirostris* is even more specialized for picking coral polyps.

The strong teeth of the parrot fishes are proof of their eating habits. Most species bite off pieces of coral and grind them up to gain nourishment from the algae growing on them. Other species eat hard weeds.

A school of young striped catfish. When threatened they form a compact mass, their tails in the center and their whiskered heads radiating outwards.

193

Another butterfly fish species found on the reefs of the Red Sea, Indian Ocean and Pacific.

The porcupine fish also has strong 'teeth'. In this fish the teeth have grown together to form hard plates, perfectly adapted for cracking the hard shells of the crabs, snails and sea urchins on which it feeds. The porcupine fish is characterized by its spines which lie flat all over its body under normal conditions but stick out like a porcupine's under stress. As soon as it senses danger the porcupine fish swallows water very quickly: this puffs out its body and makes the spines stand out sharply.

Surgeon fishes also defend themselves with their spines. The 'knives' normally lie flat at the base of the fish's tail, but when it is attacked they stand out and the wildly lashing tail of the surgeon fish can cut very deep wounds.

Trigger fishes have spines with a special mechanism to keep the spines stiff in rough water. The first dorsal fin is modified into two spines, the first of which is very large and strong and the second quite small. The spines fit smoothly into a groove in the fish's back while it is quietly swimming around. Then when it is seeking rest, or when it gets frightened, the trigger fish swims into a coral shelter and sets the mechanism; the large spine is erected and then locked into position by the small spine which falls into a special groove

behind it. This locking mechanism ensures that the spine will stay in its most effective position during a fight or in rough seas. It can only be unlocked when the small trigger is released.

Trigger fishes can be very bizarre in coloring and one species has been called the 'Picasso' fish. All trigger fishes have strong teeth for crushing the shells of crustaceans, sea urchins and mollusks. They will chase small and sick animals and have the horrible habit, common to many predators, of starting their attack on the eyes of the victim. This is the reason why so many coral fishes, the butterfly fishes in particular, have their true eyes disguised by a vertical black stripe and an imitation eye made by a blob in their skin patterns toward the tail. This deceives the enemy and gives the fish the advantage of surprise flight in an unexpected direction.

We saw how many fishes crush hard materials to get at their food and such materials will leave the fishes' bodies as dust, sinking to the bottom. Geologists have observed that the coral fishes make a large contribution to the sediment of shallow tropical waters. They even estimate this to be more than 200,000 pounds a year. The hordes of parrot fishes are the chief contributors, but surgeon fishes also swallow sand and chalk. The indigestible parts of the sand, chalk and algae

Blue surgeon fish, found mainly off the Philippine Islands, swim in large shoals.

194

mixture are pulverized in their strong stomachs and fall down through the water as dust. Both the herbivores and the carnivores feeding on mollusks, crustaceans and echinoderms, pulverizing the shells, chitineous covers and calciferous armors of their victims, add to the sediment.

Man has become a danger to the reef populations. Curious people who possess insufficient knowledge of marine life do not hesitate to equip themselves with diving apparatus and underwater guns for shooting the fish. The balance of life is disturbed and the situation is worsened when such people break off corals for souvenirs. Corals grow slowly and a reef may die within a few years if too many of the living corals are removed. Several countries have realized this and declared reefs or parts of reefs as reserves where hunting and vandalism are forbidden. Such reserves are found off the coast of Florida and the southwest of Ceylon.

Coral reefs present such rich and fascinating populations, such promising ground for further study and new discoveries, that their disappearance would be a great and shaming loss.

Trigger fishes like to find safe hiding places. Here a green trigger fish takes refuge in an old vase.

The Art of Animation

WHEN did animation begin? No one can be sure. Perhaps it was thirty thousand years ago, when an artist drew a boar on the wall of a cave in Spain. To capture the motion of the running animal, he drew it with eight legs.

Or were the Egyptians the first animators? A wall decoration of 2000 B.C. shows progressive stances of two wrestlers as they grapple with each other.

Attempts at animation can be found in the cultures of many peoples. But it was the motion picture that made it possible for drawn figures really to move.

J. Stuart Blackton was one of the pioneers of animation. In 1906, he put out a film short called *Humorous Phases of Funny Faces.* The faces, drawn on a blackboard, changed expression. Another early animator was Parisian Emile Cohl. He made a two-minute film called *Phantasmagoria.*

Winsor McCay put his comic strip character,

Little Nemo, into a cartoon film in 1908. Later, McCay toured vaudeville with *Gertie, the Trained Dinosaur.* McCay gave orders from the stage. On the screen, Gertie obeyed. The act was a sensation.

The public was enchanted by the moving cartoons, and a new industry grew up in New York to satisfy this fascination. At first the screen cartoonists drew the figures and the backgrounds for each of the thousands of frames of film that made up an animated short. Then J. R. Bray and Earl Hurd developed the system of drawing the characters on celluloid sheets. These could be photographed against a single background.

In 1923, Walt Disney came from Kansas City to Hollywood. With his brother Roy, he set up a cartoon studio and began turning out a series called *Alice in Cartoonland.* Alice was a real little girl who had adventures with cartoon characters. The series sold well, and Walt started another one starring Oswald the Rabbit. In 1928, he produced the first sound cartoon. The hero was a new character named Mickey Mouse.

That event marked the beginning of a new age. In forty years, animation progressed from relatively crude cartooning to the moving illustration of *Sleeping Beauty, Jungle Book* and *The Aristocrats*. It became an art.

How Cartooning Began

The history of the cartoon industry is so brief that there are men active in the business today who can recall the early years when animation was getting its start in New York. Dick Huemer is one of these men. He went to work for Raoul Barre in 1916, drawing Mutt and Jeff.

"Usually there were three animators on a cartoon," Dick recalls. "One of us might say, 'Let's make a picture about Hawaii.' Fine! So each of us would work on a third of the picture. A couple of weeks later, we'd make a hookup. We never bothered with plots. Cartoons were just a series of gags strung together."

Anything was possible in the world of the cartoon, but this was discovered bit by bit. Albert Hurter once animated a scene showing Mutt leaning against a railing next to a steep precipice. When the scene was photographed, the camera operator failed to include the celluloid with the railing on it. In the finished film, Mutt leaned against thin air. The law of gravity was promptly repealed in every New York studio. Cartoon characters walked on air, water, ceilings, clouds and the sides of skyscrapers.

In the early days of the Disney Studio, story creation was a simple matter. Walt and Ub Iwerks created the stories, using gags which Roy Disney had collected. Ub made sketches of the action and Walt and musician Carl Stallings timed the music, then typed the dialogue on the bottom of the sketches.

As more products were needed, most of the staff took part in story meetings. These were held

Wall decoration circa 2000 B.C. shows how Egyptians attempted animation.

197

at night in Walt's house, a five-room bungalow which would rock with laughter as Walt, Roy, Ub, Wilfred Jackson, Les Clark and Johnny Cannon concocted new adventures for the Mouse.

The studio grew and the method of story creation changed a little. Walt and his storymen would work out a story line. Then the entire studio would be invited to contribute gags and pieces of business. Those who came up with belly laughs—or even giggles—were rewarded with payments from two dollars to twenty-five.

By the early thirties, the Disney Studio was bursting with creativity. But there was a need for a better way to present stories. The need was met by the storyboard. This developed, almost by accident, in the office of Webb Smith.

"Webb was an old newspaperman and a cracking good cartoonist," Walt recalled, years later. "We'd sit in his office in the morning and think up gags. Say Pluto was tracking a caterpillar. You'd have shots of him tracking up and down hills, then maybe shots of the caterpillar on the dog's nose or tail.

"After lunch, I'd drop in Webb's office and he'd have the sequence sketched out on sheets of paper. They'd be all over the room, on desks, on the floor, everyplace. It got too tough to follow them; we decided to pin all the sketches on the wall in sequence. That was the first storyboard."

Today the storyboard is standard in the cartoon industry. Simple and basic, it tells the story exactly as the camera's eye will see it. It is flexible; changes can be made merely by unpinning sketches and substituting new ones. The storyboards show pace, movement and excitement. As camera work became more complex, the boards detailed camera angles, as can be seen from early Snow White drawings by Hurter, Charles Philippi and Hugh Hennesy.

There are usually sixty drawings to a board. No attempt is made at finished art. Sketches are bold black and white, so that they can be read across a room. Occasionally color is added to suggest a mood.

A short can usually be told in three storyboards, a feature in twenty-five or more. The

198

199

boards are photographed before the sketches are taken down, to be stored in the studio morgue.

Disney storymen confess that the boards had one drawback. As the storyman read the boards, Walt's mind could speed ahead and absorb the sketches before they could be explained.

If the storyboard came about by accident, the story department did not. Mickey Mouse was an international celebrity, but he was not paid like a movie star. Cartoon shorts were considered program fillers. Theater men would shell out only a few dollars for a cartoon.

No one knows when the Disney Studio first started gearing for the feature-length cartoons. Certainly one of the important steps was taken in

1931, when Walt began the story department. He placed Ted Sears in charge and told him: "If we're going to get better stories we'll have to split the responsibilities of the story workers and the artists. From now on, I want you to concentrate on developing stories."

Snow White started rolling in 1934. Walt had been fascinated with the story all his life.

"The figures of the dwarfs intrigued me," he said. "I thought it was a good plot with wide appeal."

He had to generate enthusiasm for the project at the studio. Would audiences hold still to watch eighty minutes of drawings on a screen? Nobody knew. And the studio had always strung cartoon

Simplicity was the keynote for Mickey's debut in "Steamboat Willie."

Cartoon stories were more complex when Donald made his debut.

stories together, gag after gag. A feature called for new techniques.

Thousands of ideas for *Snow White* were presented in story meetings over a three-year period. False starts were made. Ideas once thought brilliant were later abandoned. But bit by bit, each scene was fashioned. And in 1937, the world acclaimed *Snow White*, a motion picture which drew more money into theaters than any other picture previous to that time.

What makes a good story? According to Walt, the prime quality is heart. "It should be a simple story," he said, "with characters the audience really can care about. They've got to have a rooting interest.

"Besides heart, the story should be understandable in any country, since half our revenue comes from overseas. Nearly all our stories have that international quality. The exception was *Lady and the Tramp,* which was very American. But there you have dogs, and they're international."

The Disney subjects are generally timeless. Since production can take from three to seven years, a topical film could be out of date before its release. And reissues play a big part in the studio economy.

What makes a good storyman? First, a good memory. A good storyman never forgets a situa-tion. An incident that happened years ago might be usable in a cartoon sequence.

Nearly all storymen began as artists. They think in terms of pictures. That's how the stories are told. Dialogue is economical. Only a thousand words are heard in *Bambi,* all of them necessary to the story.

"The important thing to us is what the characters are doing, not so much what they're saying," comments Winston Hibler. "We are always thinking in terms of movement."

How is the story for a cartoon feature prepared for the screen? The answer is found in years of conferences, sleepless nights, storyboards, hallway conversations, sweat, inspiration and talent.

Why Snow White Was Chosen

Snow White offered a clean plot. It had a basic outline of a heroine menaced by her stepmother and finally rescued by a hero. The dwarfs who sheltered the girl and the animals of the forest were no problem. They harked back to the cartoon characters that had been drawn for years. The prince was difficult to animate, so his role was kept to a minimum. He appeared at the beginning and end; the idea of a dream dance with him and Snow White was discarded.

Pinocchio offered too much material. The orig-

201

"The Skeleton Dance" marked the first time action was coordinated with music.

creation of the screenplay. It is not always at the beginning. One key sequence is chosen to begin production. It is always a sequence which will give the main characters a chance to display themselves. Thus the characters are established for the remainder of the motion picture. In *Jungle Book*, for example, the first characters to come to the screen were Bagheera the panther, Mowgli the man-cub and the comic bear, Baloo. The wolves who had raised Mowgli in the jungle were not designed until the picture was nearly finished. Bagheera, Mowgli and Baloo carried the story.

Or, as one storyman put it, "Walt always liked to start in the middle and work toward both ends."

inal Collodi story rambled through a wide field of adventures. The storymen had to narrow the story down to a cohesive plot while preserving the spirit of the classic. Some changes had to be made in characterization. In the book, the puppet squashed the cricket with his wooden foot, then went out into the world as a complete and thorough delinquent. That didn't make for a sympathetic hero, so Pinocchio was altered into a well-meaning boy who was led astray by conniving characters. The cricket lived on as Pinocchio's conscience, and as the narrator of the plot.

Bambi was a complete departure from previous Disney features. It was a serious story with little opportunity for comedy. The seriousness was relieved by Thumper the rabbit and Flower the skunk.

Cinderella was another example of a clean plot. The basic pattern of the classic story was there, but something was needed. The mice solved the problem. They were comic, and they had their own sub-plot and their own villain, the cat. They also made Cinderella warmer through her compassion for them.

Peter Pan presented a wealth of material. The plot had to be tightened and some of the sentiment of the Barrie original had to be sacrificed.

The storymen have to start somewhere in the

The Characters Come To Life

"Until a character becomes a personality, it cannot be believed. Without personality, the character may do funny or interesting things, but unless people are able to identify themselves with the character, its actions will seem unreal. And without personality, a story cannot ring true to the audience."

This observation by Walt Disney is an indication of why the art of animation reached maturity at his studio. He always stressed the importance of relating cartoon characters to human experience.

Walt's predecessors in the cartoon field slighted personality. In the early days, it was enough that cartoon figures moved and did fantastic things.

There were favorites among the early cartoon characters. Felix the Cat, the clever creation of Pat Sullivan, had a way of pacing back and forth as he pondered his next move. But the rest of his repertoire was gags. Farmer Al Falfa was a human stooge amid a cast of animals. Most of the time he was the villain, and the story concerned the barnyard animals ganging up on him.

Many early cartoon figures came direct from the newspaper comics. Readers of the funny pages could recognize Jeff, the guileless short fellow, and Mutt, the tall one who was always getting him into trouble. But the newspaper cartoon figures suffered in the transition to the screen.

Animation of the human form wasn't clever enough. Audiences could get used to stylized animals cavorting about, but there was something jarring about humans making jerky, unrealistic movements.

Easy methods of drawing cartoon figures were generally known as the circle formula and the rubber-hose method.

The quick way to draw a character was to use circles—a round head, round eyes, a round body. The animator never had to worry about angles.

Arms and legs behaved like rubber hoses. No elbows, knees or wrists bothered the animator.

Winsor McCay (above, left) was the first to see the commercial possibilities of animation. His "Gertie, the Trained Dinosaur" was a hit. Earl Hurd (above, right) helped develop animation on cells. Pat Sullivan (left) invented the popular Felix, the Cat.

Illustrations show how animation is made easy. In drawing Clarabelle Cow and Clara Cluck, artists follow the outlines of interlocking circles.

Rubbery, tube-like limbs could be drawn quickly and moved in any direction, or elongated, if need be.

Creators in the first two decades of the animation industry were handicapped in another way; movies were silent. The voice is a prime method of conveying the personality of a cartoon figure. And the first animated character to have a voice was, of course, Mickey Mouse.

"Mickey was the beginning," Walt said once. "Because of Mickey, we were able to go on and attempt the things that were to make animation a real art. It was an art that was subsidized by the public's acceptance of what we were doing.

"He had to be simple. We had to push out seven hundred feet of film every two weeks, so we couldn't have a character who was tough to draw.

"His head was a circle with an oblong circle for a snout. The ears were also circles so they could be drawn the same, no matter how he turned his head.

"His body was like a pear and he had a long tail. His legs were pipestems and we stuck them

An early Mickey Mouse—the circular design made him easy to draw.

205

in big shoes to give him the look of a kid wearing his father's shoes.

"We didn't want him to have mouse hands, because he was supposed to be more human. So we gave him gloves. Five fingers looked like too much on such a little figure, so we took away one. That was just one less finger to animate.

"To provide a little detail, we gave him the two-button pants. There was no mouse hair or any other frills that would slow down animation. That made it tougher for the cartoonists to give him character."

But his character shone through, and audiences fell in love with Mickey. He was endorsed by the League of Nations and enshrined in Madame Tussaud's wax museum.

Through the years, Mickey has changed to become a more workable figure. His nose became shorter and he grew rounder and sleeker. He was given pupils instead of large dots for eyes. He grew eyebrows.

As is the case with most film stars, Mickey didn't remain on top forever. He was fundamentally a situation comic; he was not funny in himself. Other characters offered more latitude for comedy gimmicks.

Still, Mickey has made several wonderful comebacks. Millions remember his performance in *The Sorcerer's Apprentice,* and in 1955, Mouse ears sprouted on youngsters all over the nation when he appeared as the host of the Mickey Mouse Club television show.

Donald Duck was one of dozens of animal characters devised during the thirties. He was first cast for a supporting role in *The Wise Little Hen.*

The story was based on the old nursery tale about the hen who tries to get others to help her

Donald found two fine friends in Panchito and Joe Carioca in "Three Caballeros." Live action was combined with animation.

206

plant corn. All refuse, then rally around when the corn dinner is to be eaten. Donald Duck was one of the lazy fellows who disappointed the hen.

Walt felt that Donald had real possibilities. In *The Orphans' Benefit* he stole the show by reciting *Mary Had a Little Lamb* and *Little Boy Blue*, then exploding in a wild tantrum.

His performance convulsed theater-goers and he became a regular in Mickey Mouse films. As animators worked with him, the need for changes was realized. The early duck was rather tall, with stick-like legs and a long bill. He was comic, but not entirely likable.

Gradually he became squatter and more rotund. His head became bigger to provide more definition to his expressions. His eyes were developed for personality and his bill grew shorter to become more expressive.

But his voice, done by Clarence Nash, remained the same. So did his explosive personality. Mickey Mouse was not a clown, but Donald was naturally funny. He could be injected into an endless series of comic situations and story plots. Donald became the star of his own series with *Modern Inventions* in 1937. He is the most versatile of all the Disney characters; he can play any role except a gentleman or a dumbbell.

It seems illogical that a loose-jointed, dimwitted hound like Pluto could be a trailblazer in the search for believable cartoon characters. Yet it's true.

Pluto made his debut in *The Chain Gang*, a 1930 Mickey Mouse short. Later he appeared in

In "How to Ski" and "How to Play Baseball" Goofy zanily demonstrates popular sports.

another Mickey Mouse film, *The Picnic*. The dog, who was often drawn by Norm Ferguson, is credited with being the first cartoon character to break away from the old style of animation. He could reason and pantomine his thoughts.

This seems like a simple matter, but animators were long in realizing its value. In the early days, there was little real thought process. Only when cartoon characters learned to reason could they be entirely convincing.

Pluto was shown at his reasoning best in the fiypaper sequence, a classic devised by Webb Smith. Sniffing along, Pluto comes to a sheet of flypaper lying on the ground. His nose sticks to it. He figures he can get rid of the sticky paper by putting his paw on it. Then his paw is stuck. He continues taking step after step to escape, and the audience roars at his predicament.

Another dog who has seen good service over the years is Goofy, the affable halfwit. His bucktooth grin and hayseed manner endeared him immediately. Unlike Pluto, who keeps four paws on the ground, Goofy assumed human proportions and costumes, portraying human-like roles. He was known originally as Dippy Dawg, but later he was tagged Goofy.

Other supporting players have emerged in the shorts. There are Chip and Dale, the two pesky chipmunks devised to plague Donald Duck. Donald's nephews, Huey, Dewey and Louie, were introduced in 1938 and proved a welcome fixture in the duck cartoons.

Some characters failed to make the transition from the old to new methods of animation. Horace Horsecollar and Clarabelle Cow were serviceable in their time, but they were fundamentally the grotesque, rubbery characters of the old school. They couldn't change, they faded into obscurity.

A word should be said for Pegleg Pete, whose history dates back as far as Mickey's. He made his debut in *Steamboat Willie*, and appeared again and again in later shorts. A combination of alley cat and Wallace Beery, he made a capital villain—bluff, unyielding, mean as anything.

A word should also be said for a trio of pigs. In 1933, when Walt delivered the *Three Little Pigs* to distributors in New York for review, they complained. Here was a cartoon with only four characters in it. But Walt wasn't worried. Preview audiences had been enthusiastic, and each pig drew interest as an individual. Walt wrote his brother Roy: "At last we have achieved true personality in a whole picture."

The four characters were masterpieces. The pigs were round and seemed extremely edible. The two frivolous pigs looked plump, but light-footed. The industrious pig had more solid virtues, and he endeared himself by saving the playboys from the wolf.

The wolf was slinking, hairy and properly horrible, yet there was something winning about him. You had to admire his persistence, his cunning, his dauntlessness in the face of defeat.

Everything combined to make *Three Little Pigs* a hit. The characters were fresh and new. The song, *Who's Afraid of the Big Bad Wolf,* was a sensation. Color was used with great success.

The inspired character developement in *Three Little Pigs* paved the way for the personalities that were to be created in films of feature length.

Snow White was the supreme test of the ability of the Disney Studio to create characters. This time the creators were not merely devising some clever animals for a short. They had to create characters beguiling enough to hold interest for the length of a feature film.

Walt knew at once that the dwarfs would have to carry the picture. Snow White was a charming but standard heroine. The stepmother was a fairy tale villainess. The dwarfs would have to provide the comedy and human interest. They had to be good!

Walt set the story department to work on devising the seven characters. He reasoned that each would have to have sharply defined characteristics so that each would stand out. The natural thing was to pick names that were descriptive of the personalities he hoped to create for each of them.

Here are some of the names that were proposed: Jumpy, Deafy, Gabby, Nifty, Sniffy, Lazy, Stuffy, Shorty and Burby.

Among the finalists, those with the obvious characteristics were fairly easy: Grumpy, Happy, Sleepy, Sneezy and Bashful. The other two took more thought.

"For the leader, we needed a special kind of personality," recalled Walt. "He was one of those bumbling, self-appointed leaders who tries to take command but then gets all tangled up. We gave him the name of Doc. It was a good handle for a person in authority. It also suited his personality.

"Dopey was the toughest of all. The boys couldn't seem to get him at all. They tried to make him too much of an imbecile, which was not what we had in mind.

"Dopey *wasn't* an imbecile. Finally, we thought of a way to put him across: make him a human with dog mannerisms!

"That solved it. You know the way a dog will be so intent on sniffing a trail that he doesn't see the rabbit right in front of him—and when

210

the rabbit scurries away the dog does a delayed take? That's the way Dopey was. When Dopey had a dream, he pawed with his hand the way a dog does while sleeping.

"But he had to do one thing really well, or he'd just be stupid. So we had him do a clever little slaphappy dance at the dwarfs' entertainment. That let him show off his inner personality."

The extra labor on Dopey was worth the effort. He proved to be the most beguiling of the dwarfs.

Once the characters of the dwarfs were established, the seven little men were fitted with voices from among veteran performers in Hollywood. Billy Gilbert, whose sneezing routine was famous, was a natural for Sneezy. Roy Atwell, a radio comedian who specialized in mixed-up language, played Doc. Happy was veteran actor Otis Harlan and Bashful, Scotty Mattraw. Versatile Disney hand Pinto Colvig played Grumpy and Sleepy.

"We tried many voices for Dopey," said Walt. "Every one of them killed the character, so we decided not to let him talk. It wasn't that he *couldn't* talk. He just never had tried!"

Some of the story people argued that the scene in which Snow White woke up to find the dwarfs around her was too long.

"Maybe it is," replied Walt, "but we've got to take the time to have her meet each dwarf in-dividually, so the audience will get acquainted with them. Even if we bore the audience a little, they'll forget it later because they'll be interested in each individual dwarf."

Walt was right. Audiences were fascinated with each of the seven, the picture was an enormous success and the way was paved for many more magic figures to follow the dwarfs—Pinocchio, Jiminy Cricket, Dumbo, Bambi, Tinker Bell, Jock and Trusty, Captain Hook, Mr. Smee, Merlin, Baloo and a host of others.

The Characters Talk!

Sound came to the movies in 1928, when Walt was launching his new cartoon character, Mickey Mouse. He had already produced two shorts, *Plane Crazy* and *Galloping Gaucho*. Enthusiastic about the possibilities of sound, he started a third film, even though the series had not yet been sold.

It was called *Steamboat Willie*, and everything was devised for audible values with the whole picture tied together with music. The studio was pioneering all the way. There was no sound equipment available; everything had to be improvised.

"How are we going to time the drawings to the music?" Walt asked.

*Johnny Cannon, Jack Cutting, Wilfred Jackson, Ub Iwerks, and Les
Clark animating in the early days when the cartoon was learning to talk.*

Wilfred Jackson, whose mother was a piano teacher, suggested a metronome. "We know how fast the film will run—ninety feet a minute. All we've got to figure is how fast the beat of the music is, and we can break it down into frames."

The idea worked. Walt whistled *Steamboat Bill*, and Jackson played his mouth organ. The metronome measured their rhythm. Then an exposure sheet was worked out with the help of Ub Iwerks.

If the rhythm was set at sixty beats a minute, that meant a beat came every twenty-four frames, since twenty-four frames of film are projected every second. The exposure sheet which Ub devised is used today in the animation industry virtually unchanged.

One big question remained. Would sounds be convincing coming from cartoon characters on the screen? As soon as a few sequences of the picture were assembled, Walt decided to find out. The Disney staff gathered one hot September night at the studio, a converted store on Hyperion Avenue. To eliminate noise, the projector was placed outside a window. Roy was projectionist.

The audience were the studio wives and the three ladies who comprised the inking and painting department. The screen was a bed sheet at the other end of the room.

Behind a glass door on the other side of the bed sheet were the other members of the staff. They stood before a microphone that Ub had improvised from a telephone and a radio, and as they watched the flickering figures on the screen, they responded to the cues. Jackson played his mouth organ. Ub and Les Clark beat on pans and boxes. Johnny Cannon made animal sounds. Walt operated ten-cent store noise-makers and spoke a few words of dialogue.

It worked! The illusion was successful. The cartoon makers finished the picture in high spirits.

But now they had to record the sound track on the film.

There was no equipment in Hollywood, so Walt tucked the film and the score under his arm and headed for New York.

At the end of a costly recording session with thirty musicians, the score came out too long. Also, the bass fiddle kept blowing out tubes. Once

212

Walt himself ruined a take by coughing into the microphone.

Walt wired Roy to scrape together more money to finance another scoring session. This time there were only eighteen musicians. At last the score came out even—moos, oinks, whistles and all. The first sound cartoon was completed and proved a sensation with audiences everywhere.

With the mechanics of sound conquered, there remained an aesthetic question: how should the characters sound?

During the early Mickey cartoons, Walt supplied the occasional exclamations the little fellow uttered. But when the series began to catch on and longer dialogue was possible, Walt figured he should hire an actor to do Mickey's voice. He sent for one to audition for the role.

"How do you want the mouse to talk?" the puzzled actor asked.

Walt explained. "It's a high falsetto, but not squeaky. Do you get what I mean?"

The actor tried, but he didn't get it. Finally someone said, "Look, Walt, you can do the voice exactly the way you want it. Why don't you be Mickey?"

Walt pondered. It was true. What's more, Walt would always be there. From that day forward, Walt's voice was Mickey.

Once Walt heard an animal imitator on a Los Angeles radio show. He listened to the peculiar noises and exclaimed, "That's a duck!" He quickly called the station to learn the entertainer's name.

The man was Clarence Nash. He worked for a local milk company, visiting schools in the company's uniform and driving a miniature milk wagon pulled by ponies. He amused the kids with bird calls and talks about wild life and finished with *Mary Had a Little Lamb* as recited by a duck.

When Donald Duck made his debut in *Wise Little Hen,* Nash provided the voice. He has been doing Donald ever since.

The advent of feature cartoons made the selection of voices even more important. Snow White had to be charming without being comic. Her voice had to sound real, yet it needed a fairy tale quality.

213

Clarence Nash

Verna Felton

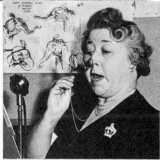

Sterling Holloway

Adriana Caselotti

Barbara Luddy

For weeks, Walt listened to girl singers. He had a microphone connected from the sound stage to his office. He listened there, because he didn't want the singer's appearance to affect his choice.

One day a voice came over and Walt said, "That's the girl." She was Adriana Caselotti. She had been reared in the operatic tradition and could do birdlike trills that were needed for Snow White.

The casting of voices has become no easier than it was in *Snow White* days. Says casting man Jack Lavin: "The trouble is that the production men themselves don't know what they are looking for until they find it. They may go through hundreds of voices before they say, There—that's the quality we're looking for!"

There are several favorite Disney actors, most of them graduates of radio, who are used again and again because of the rare comic and human qualities in their voices. Sterling Holloway was the Cheshire Cat in *Alice in Wonderland*, Kaa the python in *The Jungle Book*, and he had the title role in *Winnie the Pooh*.

Bill Thompson, the "Old Timer" of the Fibber McGee and Molly radio show, is another favorite. He was Smee in *Peter Pan* and Jock in *Lady and the Tramp*.

Verna Felton, once Red Skelton's grandma on radio, gave her voice and appearance to the fairy godmother in *Cinderella*. She also did the voice for the Queen of Hearts in *Alice in Wonderland*, and Flora in *Sleeping Beauty*.

Eleanor Audley became a Disney expert on villainous females. Among her memorable characters have been the queen in *Snow White,* the stepmother in *Cinderella,* and Maleficent in *Sleeping Beauty*.

In the early sound cartoons, characters said such lines as "Hey," "Look," "Ouch" and "Hello!" The animator's work was simple. All he had to do was open the character's mouth for an ejaculation.

But sound equipment improved, and Mickey and his pals began using sentences. Animators found themselves staring into mirrors to observe how the mouth works.

Snow White ushered in the era of real dialogue.

214

Elenor Audley

Snow White, the witch and the dwarfs had to deliver all kinds of lines—straight as well as gag—and do them convincingly.

How is this done?

The story department originates the dialogue and business of a scene. A search is made for the right voices to fit the characters. When the actors are found, they are given a thorough rundown on the scene from the storyboards. This gets them in the proper mood. Then the lines are recorded.

A phonograph record of the dialogue goes to the animator. He also gets an exposure sheet on which is a reading of the recording by a cutter. It gives the exact number of frames required for each syllable and points out where the accents fall.

For instance, Ollie Johnston, who with Frank Thomas animated Flora, Fauna and Merryweather in *Sleeping Beauty,* was given an exposure sheet with the line, "It isn't that, dear." The sheet told him that Flora had to deliver the line within the space of thirty-four frames.

"But it's not just a matter of opening and closing the mouth," says Johnston. "You have to consider the personality of Flora, her mood when she says the line, her character. In this case, she would speak with a sympathetic shake of the head.

"In a closeup, we try to do things with the eyes and the rest of the face as well as with the mouth. For instance, you get an idea and your eyes begin to widen. Your cheeks start to come up. Your whole face moves."

In the early days of sound cartoons, sound effects men were expert percussionists. They had to be. Music, voices and effects were recorded on one track in one session, and the noises had to be timed perfectly. This required great ingenuity. Within a running time of six or seven minutes they had to produce dozens of different noises, following cues which were written into the musical score ("Eight bars of flutes, followed by a window pane shattering.")

Tricks were soon discovered. The crinkling of cellophane sounded like a roaring fire. The crushing of a berry basket sounded like splintering

ABOVE: *forest fire in "Bambi" is produced on the sound track by crinkling cellophane close to the microphone.* BELOW: *Jim MacDonald crushes strawberry boxes to make the sound for splintering wood.*

wooden planks. A great crash might be produced by tumbling a pile of crates and drums.

One of the first sound effects men at the studio was Jim McDonald, who had played drums with dance bands in Los Angeles. Short, intense, with amazing skill in his fingers, he has produced sounds for Disney cartoons for more than thirty-five years.

His toughest assignment?

"I guess it was when they asked me for the noise of a spider web shimmering," he says. "I said to myself, how would a spider web shimmer? I went out to the shop and found pieces of dural-uminum. I picked a dozen pieces for each note and collected an entire scale."

Makers of the dragon sequence in *Sleeping Beauty* needed a sound for the fiery breath of the monster. They asked the United States Army for some training films and found precisely the right sound—a flame thrower!

Frank Churchill leads the orchestra as Walt listens behind him.
In those days, music and effects had to be recorded in one take.

Mickey Makes Music

Music was wed to the Disney cartoons from the first moment *Steamboat Willie* came around the bend. It so dominated the early sound cartoons that the animator and musician worked in the same office. It contained a piano as well as desks and was called the music room.

In those days, music was a despot. The musician put the songs and tuneful bits together and handed the score to the animator. The animator timed the music on his exposure sheet and fashioned the action to fit.

The songs were usually public domain tunes like *Turkey in the Straw* and *Old McDonald Had a Farm*. One venture into the classical was the sextette from *Lucia* as sung by the operatic hen, Clara Cluck (the voice belonged to veteran actress Florence Gill). Not until Frank Churchill's *Big Bad Wolf* hit from *Three Little Pigs* did the

cartoon makers capitalize on the value of original song material.

The influence of Paul Whiteman in the early cartoon scores was noted by Paul Smith, who started as a Disney arranger in 1933 and has scored most of the nature films. The music had the syncopated beat that made Whiteman a commanding figure in the jazz age. By its very nature, the cartoon score developed apart from the musical backgrounds of live-action movies. It became known as "Mickey Mouse music" and was not highly considered by more serious artists. It was dominated by percussion and sound effects. It stemmed from circus bands and can-can music. The vaudeville drummer was an expert at such music after years of snare drum rolls and tympani wallops for jugglers and acrobats.

Gradually, Mickey Mouse music became refined and demonstrated its worth. Film composers in live-action films saw the value of

synchronizing music to action, especially in comedy and suspense scenes.

In the earliest years of the studio, the Silly Symphonies were a great stride forward in the use of music. The first, made in 1929, was called *The Skeleton Dance*. Originally it was to be animated to Saint-Saens' *Danse Macabre*, but the rights couldn't be cleared. Carl Stallings composed another piece with graveyard atmosphere.

Ub Iwerks animated the action with great imagination. Four skeletons cavorted in a wild dance until the cock's crow sent them back into their graves.

Some thought the subject would be too gruesome for audiences. Walt didn't think so. At the preview, the theater rocked with laughter.

The film was another landmark in animation. For the first time, the entire action of a cartoon

An early cartoon hit—Florence Gill and Clarence Nash singing as Clara Cluck and Donald Duck.

was synchronized to a complete musical score. Ten years later, the world was to see the fruition of that discovery, a musical achievement titled *Fantasia*.

It may have been in a box at the Hollywood Bowl that Walt first heard *The Sorcerer's Apprentice*. The piece appealed to him. It told a story and it had punch. Walt bought the rights for a Mickey short.

But the cartoon ran to fifteen minutes. A costly cut of five or seven minutes was required to pare it down to the length of a short. The music and the story would suffer for it.

Then Walt met Leopold Stokowski at a Hollywood party. "I understand you are doing *The Sorcerer's Apprentice*," the conductor remarked. "I would love to conduct it for you."

Stokowski came to the studio the next day and was enthusiastic about the work that had been done on Mickey and the Sorcerer. Out of the enthusiasm of Stokowski and Walt came the idea for an anthology of serious music illustrated by animation. Deems Taylor came to Hollywood to act as the liaison between Stokowski and Disney.

As Stokowski explained, writing in a later article: "In making *Fantasia* the music suggested the mood, the coloring, the design, the speed, the

Toccata and Fugue in D Minor by Bach was different. "Here we were dealing with pure music," Walt explained. "There was no story, nothing to go on but our imaginations. We would play the music over and over and try to see what images were created in our minds."

The Scorerer's Apprentice was recorded in Hollywood and the other numbers were done in Philadelphia. *Toccata and Fugue* was reproduced exactly as Bach wrote it, but most of the other pieces were rearranged and re-orchestrated.

Fantasia was costly, and it was controversial from the start. Bosley Crowther of the New York Times called it terrific, delightful and exciting, but some critics jumped on it. They complained about tampering with the classics and declared they did not want to be shown how to envision music.

The picture was not a financial success at first, but it turned a profit in later years. New generations are discovering it as a novel excursion into the world of music. It has proven the value of experiment.

character of motion of what is seen on the screen. Disney and all of us who worked with him believe that for every beautiful musical composition, there are beautiful pictures. Music by its nature is in constant motion, and this movement can suggest the mood of the picture it invokes.

Walt and most of the creators on the picture were not musicologists. They brought to the music their own imaginations, unhampered by a reverence for the musical score. Some of the selections immediately suggested pictorial themes. Beethoven's *Pastoral* became a merry romp with fauns, centaurs and centaurettes, interrupted by the thunder of the gods. Stravinsky's *Rite of Spring* was a fearsome prehistoric scene of monsters battling. Ponchielli's *Dance of the Hours* suggested a comic ballet of ostriches, hippos, elephants and alligators.

220

The Director's Duties

Ask a director what he does and you may get the explosive answer, "He does everything!"

The director in live-action films has the ultimate responsibility for what takes place on the screen. He constructs the scene. He tells the actors what to do. He selects camera angles and paces the action.

The animation director performs much the same function, but his problems are more complex. In the beginning, animation was a one-man job. The animator drew everything in every drawing of the short.

Production in the earliest days of the Disney Studio was Walt's responsibility. When the job became too much for one man, Ub Iwerks joined him. As work increased, Walt became the first director at the studio.

He helped create the story, made rough sketches for animators to work from and followed the film through to the end.

Today, the director is generally present when the first storyboards are prepared. Once a project is given the go-ahead, he swings into action. It is his job to get that story to the screen.

He must determine how to stage each scene. The storyboards help, but they are concerned largely with telling the plot in general terms. The director must juggle the complex factors of camera angles, closeups and longshots to tell the story smoothly, dramatically and humorously. He is aided by the storymen, sketch artists and layout men.

Many scenes will require live-action shooting to guide the animators. The director must cast the actors and stage the scene. He and the storymen order whatever songs and music and sound effects must be pre-recorded. The director supervises the final setting of the characters' appearances by the sketch artists and animators. He oversees the backgrounds, and he hands the scenes out to the animators.

Large chunks of his day are spent in the projection room, which is called a "sweat box" at

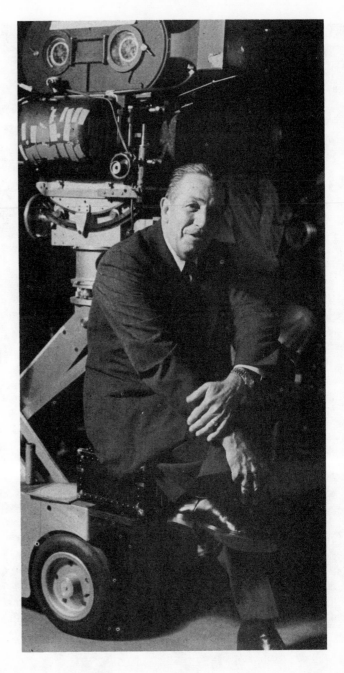

the studio. For each scene he may have to see and approve rough animation which demonstrates how the action will flow, clean-up tests (with penciled outlines complete and the action appearing as it will in the final version) and color dailies (which are color prints returned from the lab for final approval).

Throughout the long process, the director must keep the over-all picture in mind. Do the figures play well against the backgrounds? Does the plot continue to progress? Do all the elements combine and fit perfectly into the total effect?

When the color print has been assembled, the director supervises the final composite sound track. He must be sure that the voices are clear, the sound effects well placed and the music rich. The final scoring is done and the picture is cut. After the lab returns the answer print—the completed film in proper color—the picture is ready to be released. The director's duties are over. But by then he is probably already up to his elbows in a new project which will take him down the same path.

Walt was the first director at the Disney Studio, and it is a position he never abdicated. Though he became head of a vast and diversified enterprise, he performed some functions of the director to the very end of his life. Part of his last day at the studio was spent in the sweat box, checking dailies on *The Jungle Book*.

Staging The Scene

We have seen how animation has grown from a one-man operation into an industry requiring scores of creators. Layout is one of the results of that diversification. The layout man is the one who actually stages the scenes. He is responsible for how the picture looks, just as the art director decides the appearance of a live-action movie or a designer the appearance of a stage play. The layout man also moves the actors about, deciding how to photograph them for the best possible exposition of the story. He must know camera angles and how they can be used in animation. He must conceive architecture, furniture, props. He must know color, how to use it dramatically, how to assure that animation will not clash with the background.

The layout man's desk is hard by the director's, and they confer constantly. They stare at the storyboards for hours, discussing how to break

For greater dramatic effect the viewers see Lady making her flight—with her big ears flapping—from the dogs point of view.

the action down into individual scenes. Sometimes the storyboards can be followed closely. Often details must be filled in.

Some pictures present more problems than others. Mac Stewart, veteran layout artist, recalls that *Lady and the Tramp* was difficult because it was always at dog-level.

. "When you have to keep your camera down low, the picture can become static. Also, at that level there aren't many props to work with."

The layout man begins his work by making thumbnail sketches of how the scenes will be staged. Then he creates a rough layout. He directs an artist in the making of a sketch which traces in blue pencil the key positions of the characters as they move in the scene. Thus the layout man can check the size and perspective of the figures in all moves.

The layout man gives the animator drawings showing the extent of the action, drawings of the props and rough sketches of the background.

He must also give the background man a drawing showing the scope of the action. He may assist in filming live action as a guide for animation. He okays the color and sees that the backgrounds have been prepared as the animation is inked and painted, so they may be combined for the camera.

When Walt entered the cartoon feature field, he knew he would have to compete with live-action producers. He had to gain an illusion of reality in a feature. He had to make the audience forget the essential flatness of the painted characters and backgrounds. Only when scenes appeared to have depth would they seem to be real. In addition, he sought to create scenic effects that couldn't be achieved by mere drawings on cells—water ripples, fire, smoke.

Disney craftsmen set to work in the middle thirties to create a device that would get Walt what he wanted. The result was the multiplane camera.

Cartoons are normally filmed with cells stacked on top of the background, then photographed from above with a stop-motion camera. All well and good. But what happens when you want to move the camera in closer?

Suppose you have a scene of a farmhouse on a hill with a big moon behind it. You move the camera closer to the house and the house grows bigger. But so does the moon!

John Hench is a layout man whose work with the multiplane camera goes back to its earliest days. "We couldn't control the elements at infinity," he says. "We could make the foreground elements bigger, but we couldn't keep the moons the same size."

The multiplane camera solved all this. It shoots from above, like an ordinary animation camera, but the elements in the picture are not packed on

top of each other. They are placed on glass frames which are spaced twelve inches to three feet apart.

On the bottom layer is the background. On the next layer might be a row of trees. On the next, a fence. The next might be the animated layer, say a prince and princess walking. On the top layer, some shrubbery in the foreground.

Thus the camera can pull in toward the couple and the shrubbery will fall out of the scene. The couple may walk off and the camera moves in past the fence to a tree, where an owl alights.

The multiplane camera stretches to the top of a high-ceilinged room in the camera department. Each cell level is lighted individually. The lights must be adjusted carefully to assure the same colors with each exposure.

The short, *The Old Mill,* was the first to test the new camera. The camera was still in the experimental stages during *Snow White.* It came into its own in *Pinocchio.* The opening scene over the rooftops of the village was a masterpiece of camera movement, involving as many as twelve different planes in the camera.

Multiplane camera scenes are devised by the layout man. He must juggle at least five planes and keep them all in proper depth and perspective.

First, he studies the entire scene. He figures what elements of the landscape will be at infinity; that is the bottom layer. He figures out the landmarks that appear next closer to the eye; they are the next layer. He continues until he arrives at the elements in the immediate foreground.

It is tedious, exacting work, but worth all the trouble for the dramatic effect that is achieved in the film.

How The Animator Works

One of the hardest things for an outsider to visualize is how an animator works. Most people think in terms of individual drawings. How can you create hundreds of drawings that can be combined in sequence and projected to come alive on the screen?

First, the supervising animator helps design the characters. This is important; an animator should work with characters with whom he is sympathetic.

Before embarking on a sequence, the animator goes over the storyboards with the director. Any major changes in the action must be agreed upon at this stage. With the action thoroughly planned, the director, animator and head layout man confer on the mechanics of the scene. Where should the cuts be made? When does the camera pan?

The animator is given a rough layout that shows the extent of the background, the size of the characters and the extremes to which they move. He also has an exposure sheet which indicates the timing of the action and dialogue.

So armed, the animator sits down at his desk. It is a cheerless sight—all that blank paper and those sharpened pencils. Now the work begins!

Suppose the animator has a scene from *Cinderella*, as Ward Kimball once did. Lucifer the cat must sneak across a room, stop at a mouse hole, peek in and put his paw inside to grab a mouse. Inside the hole, the mice flip a trap on his paw. The cat leaps into the air and exits.

First, the animator must devise a sneaky walk. He might invent one from memory, or he might watch live-action stock footage of domestic cats stalking prey.

Does he want a fast sneak or a slow sneak? A fast one might put over the idea of cunning better. He uses a stop watch or metronome to calculate how long the sneak will take. Two seconds? That means forty-eight frames.

He also times how fast each paw would work. He arrives at the formula of one set every six frames. He knows that the right paw is on the floor on frame one, the left on frame six. The drawing begins.

The animator works at a board that is tilted at a forty-five degree angle. The center of the board is a metal circle which can be rotated to place the drawing at any angle. The circle contains a glass rectangle that can be lighted from beneath. This allows the animator to place one or more drawings over a background and see how they will combine on the screen. He draws on medium grade bond paper that is thin enough to be semi-transparent. At the bottom of the paper are two slotted holes and a round one spaced an equal distance apart. These correspond to pegs on the board. The pegs are standard throughout the studio, assuring that the animator's drawing will be in the same position when it is inked or Xeroxed on cells, painted and placed under the camera.

The animator creates sixteen or twenty key drawings of Lucifer's prowl, showing the paws in the up and down positions.

When Lucifer comes to the hole, he must pause there. For a foot and a half, he sits with body contracted, rolling his eyes menacingly. One drawing might suffice for that. Then the cat lowers his head. The animator draws only the extremes of the move. The paw goes into the hole with a swift move. Rather than switch to the mice inside, the animator may save that scene until later and go ahead with the cat's reaction to the trap. For such a violent action, he will need to make more drawings, since a greater number of extremes are needed.

The animator generally works with several

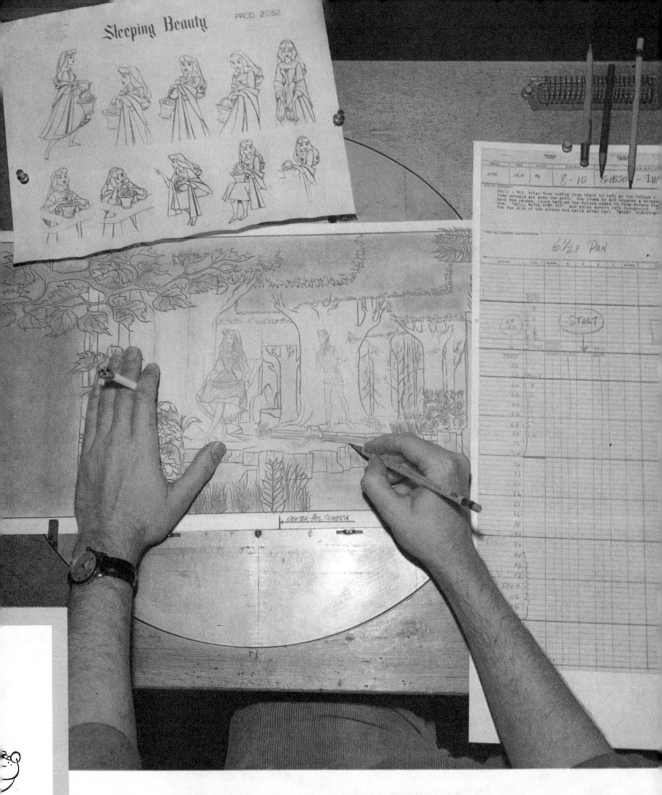

The view from the animator's chair. Animator lines up characters (in red) on layout (blue) for staging and relative size. He consults model sheet of character (above) to maintain consistent design. Sheet at right shows him the number of frames of film allotted to action in the scene.

drawings on his board. He is constantly flipping the papers to get an impression of how the action will look on the screen.

When he is finished with his work, he hands the rough drawings to his assistant, who fills in with more rough drawings to complete the action. The rough animation is photographed so the animator can see if changes should be made.

Next the scene is sent to cleanup, where the lines are put into final form by the assistant animator.

The next step is the breakdown man, an artist who creates the intermediate drawings between the extremes made by the assistant animator.

Finally, the in-betweener fills in the gaps left by the breakdown man, completing the necessary sixteen frames for each foot of film, and at last the animator's work is ready to be inked and painted.

To the animator, live-action film can be an aid, especially in animating humans. Everyone knows how humans stand and walk and move their heads. If the animator cannot duplicate that movement there would not be a convincing picture.

Even such a simple matter as rising from a chair is important. In the old days, a cartoon figure would simply rise to an erect position and walk away. But that isn't how people move. By studying live-action film, the animator can see that the figure leans forward in the chair, places his hands on the chair arms and pushes himself into a standing position.

"The important thing is to use live action as a guide, not a crutch," said Walt. "When we first started using it, some animators tried to copy the live action exactly. Their work was cramped and stilted.

"The fact is that humans can't move as freely, gracefully and comically as we can make animated figures move. We are not in the business of duplicating human action. We can do better than that—much better."

The top animators use live action as Walt suggested—as a guide. Most of them prefer scenes in which their imaginations can run rampant without concern for realistic human actions. But with features, live action is often needed as a reference.

Snowstorm effect created for "Bambi" scene.

Glimmering dandelion effect in "Fantasia."

The frame shows the intricate design created for a simple drop of water in a pool. Fast-action photos of live action were studied.

228

Mowgli
2179

Josh Meador studies bubbling vat before creating lava effects for "Fantasia."

Close-up character movement is extremely difficult to capture in live action. "No matter how good they are, actors can seldom give you exactly what you want," comments Frank Thomas. Milt Kahl agrees: "The best use of live action is for ideas—little pieces of movement that an actor does and which might not occur to you."

For scenes in which there is much rapid or intricate movement, photostats of the movie frames are made so the animator can study them closely. For other scenes, he might run the film on the moviola in his office. No matter which method he uses, he is still faced with the task of interpreting the scene in his own way with pencil and paper.

For the effects animators, it is sometimes a different story. The effects men are the ones who create raindrops, earthquakes, lightning and forest fires—to name just a few specialties. The magic of Merlin is nothing compared to the wonders that effects animators can produce.

Walt instituted the animation effects department in the thirties when he realized he needed better tools to tell the stories he dreamed of. Not everything could be created with pencil and paper.

The Disney researchers experimented with colored cells, camera diffusion (blurring focus), filming through frosted or rippled glass. Many discoveries were simple. Many are too complex to be understood by the layman. All contributed to more believable, exciting story telling.

The development of the multiplane camera was a great advance in securing animation effects. Many effects could be managed only when the cell level could be isolated from the rest of the action. The proving ground for the discoveries in effects was *The Old Mill* (1935). There was scarcely any story. There was merely an abandoned mill inhabited by mice, birds, bats and an owl. A storm came up and threatened their home, then subsided, leaving them safe.

The animation effects men gave it everything they had—lightning, rain, ripples, clouds, sun rays and firefly glows. It was so effective that it won an Academy Award that year.

With *The Old Mill*, Walt was assured that animation had grown up enough for a feature. Part of the impact of *Snow White* was due to the compelling effects—the sparkle of jewels in the mine, the horrible concoctions of the witch, the soap bubbles in the washing scene.

Effects animators are remarkable. They sit at their drawing boards surrounded by photographs of atom blasts, lightning bolts and gas explosions. Their business is to present things in an unreal way to make them seem real. Lightning, for example, is not convincing if it is drawn as it actually appears in a photograph. But by exaggerating the bolt and filling the screen with intermittent blank white frames, the effects artist can make truly startling lightning.

For *Rite of Spring*, Josh Meador found a way to show mud pots breaking and splashing. He mixed a gummy mess of oatmeal, mud and coffee grounds in a vat, then attached air hoses to send bubbles through it. The action was caught by high-speed cameras. Individual frames were processed on cells and dyed red against a yellow background. Animation was added to broaden the action. Thus for a few fleeting seconds, the audience saw primeval convulsions of the earth's surface projected on the screen.

Background and Color

The background artist is by no means low man on the totem pole. He is in at the earliest stages of a production. In fact, he can be a major factor in the creation of a feature picture. The noted illustrator Mary Blair provided inspiration in the early stages of *Alice in Wonderland, Saludos Amigos, Johnny Appleseed, Song of the South, Wintertime* and other Disney pictures.

In such instances, the background artist is also a stylist. But in either capacity, he performs one of the most important functions in the production of the film.

The layout man establishes the field of action and outlines the appearance of the set. The background man must make it visually attractive.

"Usually the theme, locale and period of the

picture give you the start," explains Claude Coats. "In *Pinocchio* we could borrow from the designs of northern Italy, Switzerland and Austria. We needed an alpine village, and this meant rich architecture with a lot of carved wood.

"In *Alice in Wonderland* the atmosphere was unreal, so we could let ourselves go with some wild designs.

"But in *Lady and the Tramp* we were dealing with real dogs. The backgrounds had to sustain that illusion of reality. The period was turn-of-the-century America, so we made much use of porch furniture of that era, plus the gingerbread ornamentation of the houses."

The background, like the musical score, should complement the action and contribute to the over-all effect. Between seven and nine hundred backgrounds are needed for an animated feature, and each must create the illusion of reality (or fantasy) without flaws. In addition, the characters must "read" well before the backgrounds.

Today, of course, all finished backgrounds—and characters—are in color. In the early days, color in animation had to wait until science made it possible.

Walt was half-way through a new Silly Symphony called *Flowers and Trees* when he saw tests of Technicolor's new three-color process. It

was what he had been waiting for. He junked what had already been done in black and white on *Flowers and Trees* and started anew.

The colors of *Flowers and Trees* may seem crude by today's standards, but they were immensely effective in 1932, when the impact of color was first being felt by movie audiences.

The advent of color brought a new dimension to animation—and also new problems. It was simple to make characters legible in black and white. The use of color required close coordination between the animated characters and the background. A red character against a purple background might induce biliousness. A green figure standing before a green tree might disappear into the foliage.

The issue is often met by keeping the characters in lively colors and graying out the backgrounds. Sometimes the formula can be reversed. An effective scene in *Snow White* was created when the dwarfs marched home from the mine, their small figures outlines in gray silhouette against a brilliant sky.

Snow White was done in muted colors, yet it was extremely successful. The triumph was in the interiors, which were underpainted in gray tones to give the woodwork a rich, fairy-tale quality.

With *Pinocchio*, the studio became a little

"Flowers and Trees" (1932) first used color in a cartoon. It was a love story of two trees.

Grace Bailey confers with Mary Tebb and Jane Considine in the Color Model Department—and Katherine Kerwin and Steve McAvoy discuss a new color with Grace Bailey.

bolder with color. *Dumbo,* with its circus background, called for gay splashes of color. Yet contrasts had to be made. One sequence showed the elephants and roustabouts struggling in the rain to set up the circus. All was gray and murky. But then the sun came out and the midway was alive with bright color.

Across from the Animation Building is the Ink and Paint Building. It is still called Ink and Paint, although precious little inking has been done there in recent years. Instead of tracing the animator's penciled line drawings on transparent celluloid with opaque ink, the ladies in the Ink and Paint Building transfer the drawings by using a Xerox machine. Thus one tedious step is eliminated from the hand-drawn animation process.

Painting—adding color to the cells—is still a custom operation.

Head of the ink and paint department is attractive Grace Turner. Without a trace of feminine bias, she explains why her sex has a monopoly in the department:

"They used men in the early days of the studio, but their work was inclined to be sloppy. Painting is precision work that requires neatness and patience. Women seem to have those qualities."

She told how the final steps are taken to complete the animation. After the animator and his crew have finished their work, a color model girl pulls out representative drawings. Consulting with the production unit, she makes copies of the drawings, creating two to six color combinations.

When the colors are chosen by the production unit, the animation drawings and exposure sheets are checked. The bundles of drawings go to Xerox, to be transferred to cells, then to the long, sunlit painting rooms, where girls fill in the Xeroxed outlines with color. The painters work on ten cells at a time, painting on the bottom side and keeping the cells in a rack before them. They do all of one color on a cell, then wait for it to dry before starting on a second color.

A chemist mixes pigment, water and certain other ingredients to produce the paints. Variations of each color are necessary for different cell levels. The cell nearest the camera will photograph its own shades, but the colors will darken under three or four layers of celluloid, so the lower cell levels must be painted brighter.

After painting, the cells are checked for accuracy and color by the supervisor. Then they are sent to the camera department for the final step in production.

That's animation—the art of animation.

233

Japan

Dᴜʀɪɴɢ the golden age of discovery, while many nations were engaged in exploration and expansion, the island empire of Japan stood aloof from the rest of the world. Throughout long centuries of isolation, the Japanese people went their separate way, evolving traditions, customs and manners all their own.

It was not until the mid-nineteenth century that Japan reluctantly and hesitantly opened her doors to the Western world. Then the sight of many scientific marvels excited the interest of the alert and clever Japanese. In the short space of a single century, they have made phenomenal technical progress and have risen to a prominent position among the family of nations, especially in commerce and industry.

Still, the Japanese cling to the gracious and charming manners and customs of their past. And in these customs which have endured, we glimpse the true soul of Japan.

Rɪᴄᴇ ᴘᴀᴅᴅɪᴇꜱ. It is in the rural areas that the past lives on most vividly, and nowhere more so than in the rice paddies. The low dikes around the small flooded paddies are still tamped firm with hoes; the young rice plants are still poked into place in the sodden ground beneath the shallow pool one at a time, by hand. Down the flooded rows move lines of laborers, each carrying a dwindling bundle of young rice plants. But these are no hired workmen; these are the owner and his family and neighbors, owners of adjoining paddies perhaps. For all help each other in planting the rice when the proper day arrives. Co-operation is a basic element in the lives of the people of rural Japan. Together the men walk the endless treadmill of the paddlewheel pumps which keep the waters at the proper depth around the growing rice.

These workers live in the same small village, a cluster of simple houses not far from their fields. There they share much of their lives; the family washing is done sociably with a stomping of feet beside the stream or pool. The children play together and wash themselves companionably.

234

Most of all, the people like to join in celebrating festivals. For ceremony is close to the heart of Japanese life. To ensure a good harvest, hard labor alone would never seem enough to a proper Japanese. It is necessary also to enlist the good will of the ancestors. For the souls of the departed, so they believe, can prevent typhoons, droughts and other devastations. And to enlist their good will, a spectacular lantern-balancing ceremony is held in certain localities.

Lanterns are an indispensable feature of many festivals, for they light the way for the spirits of the family dead as they return to earth for reunions with living members of the clan. For this particular festival, the lanterns are hung on "kantos." The kanto is a long bamboo pole with eight or nine horizontal ribs from which paper lanterns are hung. It is designed to represent an ear of rice or a pile of rice bales, with each lantern a grain or a bale. The pole may be as much as fifty feet long, the lanterns numbering twenty-six to forty-eight. The weight is from ninety-nine to a hundred thirty-two pounds.

All the young men of the town take part, bankers, storekeepers, government employees, as well as the workers in the rice paddies. The higher the pole can be raised, the taller the grain will grow, it is said; so every effort is made to raise the pole on high, balancing it on hands, foreheads, shoulders, mouths or hips, even walking on stilts in order to add to the height of the pole and, symbolically, of the grain. A trophy is awarded to the most skillful at wooing the spirits by bobbing lanterns aloft.

THE PROUD SAMURAI. The festival is a success; the spirits of the ancestors smile upon the rice-paddy workers and grant a bounteous harvest. And when the harvest has been gathered in, the time comes once more to put the burdens of the present aside, to stop the clock on the seven-day week and take time out to celebrate.

This time, for a brief moment, the glories of an honored past will be recaptured. The most honored and most heroic figures of Japanese history were the Samurai warriors, national heroes com-

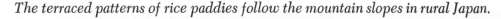

The terraced patterns of rice paddies follow the mountain slopes in rural Japan.

These farmers are using the same kind of crude plow their ancestors used to cultivate rice.

When the work in the flooded rows of the rice paddies is finished, there will be a festival.

The swordmaster, here seen examining a new blade, is the master of an ancient craft.

parable to the feudal knights in armor of Western lore. Today a chapter from their valorous past is being re-created, with costumes handed down from Samurai ancestors—both uniforms for the men and saddles for their mounts. For the Samurai, who loved the thrill of battle, were noted for their fine horsemanship.

The costumes are regulated according to each man's heritage, down to the last sash. And certainly no one but the direct descendant of a Samurai warrior would think of wearing a Samurai sword! For the sword of the Samurai was the embodiment of his knighthood. His honor and manhood were involved in every stroke of its keen blade.

Because the Samurai sword was sacred to its owner, secrets of the carefully guarded craft of the swordmaker have been handed down from father to son for almost ten centuries. Today the swords are still made entirely by hand, with all the reverence and expert care of the thirteenth and fourteenth century craftsmen who brought the techniques to perfection.

Since the making is still a religious rite, the maker first purifies himself by taking a cold shower, then visits the altar in the traditional costume of his craft before going to his forge.

Here his raw material is waiting, a clump of special coarse iron ore about the size of a baseball; this he tempers to steel. A mixture of clay, powdered coal and water is poured over the ore in the forging process. Then this mass is heated cherry red in a fire fed with special charcoal, and beaten into an even, thin sheet roughly resembling a blade. In a secret series of processes, impurities and weak spots are eliminated, and the metal is cooled with a quick plunge into a tank of water. The whole task requires a high degree of skill and most delicate control. For there are no "seconds" in this trade. The sword is tested with a slash through a bundle of wet rice straw and bamboo. If it does not pass the test, it is at once destroyed. A sword blade, though merely a symbol today, no longer a fighting weapon, must be perfect for a Samurai.

The wood-block print artist first makes a design of line drawings on very thin paper.

The second step for the artist is adding color to the black-and-white proofs of his print.

WOOD-BLOCK PRINTS. The same reverence of the artisan for the tradition-hallowed techniques of his craft is found among the makers of wood-block prints. The traditional Ukiyo-e method goes back three hundred years. The artist makes his line drawing on a very thin piece of paper. This the carver places bottom-side up on a block of cherry wood, and, carefully following the artist's design, carves away the wood to leave only the lines of the drawing untouched. He inks his block of the line drawing and prints off two dozen or more "proofs" on heavy paper called "mino" paper. And back to the artist these black outlines go.

The artist uses one proof for each color he wants to have appear in the finished print. He fills in the parts of the drawing where that color is to appear. Then back go the colored sheets to the carver, who carves out the required number of blocks for the color print.

Last of all in this three-man team of craftsmen is the printer. He uses for his prints "hosho" papers covered with a thin coating of alum to prevent the colors from seeping through. The coloring materials are made with vegetable oils, and the faces of the blocks on which the colors are pressed are usually coated with rice starch

to speed up the drying. The printer takes his sheet of hosho paper, places it on the black line block and rubs the back of the paper with a special lacquered pad of bamboo fibers and paper which is called a "baren." The paper is then similarly placed in turn over one color block after another, until all the required colors have been printed

The wood-block carver removes a black proof sheet from the carved, inked block.

Young ladies of high birth are trained as hostesses in the tea ceremony.

and the picture is complete. Usually two hundred copies of the picture are made as a first printing, and another thousand copies may be made later on. Many people can thus enjoy the work of this team of three highly skilled craftsmen—the artist, the carver, and the printer of multi-colored woodblock prints.

TEA CEREMONY. Probably no people place greater emphasis on the social arts and graces than do the Japanese. Even the rite of serving tea must be performed with absolute perfection. Finishing schools, conducted by recognized masters, prepare young ladies of high birth for the future role as wives and hostesses in the tea ceremony.

The teahouse is usually located in the peaceful setting of one of the serene and lovely small gardens of Japan—where each twig, each blossom, each pebble has its own significance. A tiny door in the teahouse forces the girls to kneel and thus to come into the presence of the host with proper humility.

The master demands nothing less than this same perfection at each stage. And every detail of the ceremony is a study in delicate grace. Even the preparation of the small fire to heat the water has its own rules; the bits of charcoal must be placed with careful precision in a fire pit of clean, damp sand. And the preparation of the tea itself is a highly cherished art.

Yet the ritual is not planned as an exercise in discipline for the sake of discipline; the very perfection of the restraint is for the protection of a serene and simple beauty in both setting and deportment.

In a land so teeming with millions of people, so scant of usable acreage, a beauty-loving people can afford to leave nothing to chance. So every vista, no matter how limited in scope, each carefully pruned and trained dwarf tree, each trickling drop, becomes a symbol of a larger beauty in this frugal and lovely land. And since in the ancient Japanese religion, trees, streams and all things in nature are thought to possess "souls,"

238

even an ordinary-appearing rock can be considered a treasure. Set in a garden of swept and patterned sand, in exquisite harmony with other objects, it creates a feeling of space and peace.

A SHINTO WEDDING. Marriage too is full of symbolism. Customs are changing, but some families still cling to the old-fashioned tradition of having the parents make the matches. Though the young people may have met and been attracted to each other, a good friend of the family or a relative still acts as a proper go-between.

If the young man of the family is moré docile and has made no choice for himself, the go-between's assistance is asked at making inquiries of suitable families who are looking for husbands for their daughters. The go-between submits photographs of acceptable girls for the family's approval. If the parents of both young people seem interested in the match, a formal ceremonial tea is arranged. The parents become better acquainted; and, just incidentally, the future bride and groom meet, perhaps for the first time.

Next comes the exchange of small ceremonial gifts, among them a fan symbolizing the opening future, two bundles of white hemp threads meaning that the young couple will live together until their hair turns gray, a dried cuttlefish, symbol of a long-lived woman, and money for the purchase of a barrel of sake (rice wine).

The Shinto wedding ceremony is full of ancient and elaborate symbolism.

The evening meal of a Japanese fishing family may include a bit of a fish as a treat.

This father is helping his young son learn the difficult art of eating with chopsticks.

The groom's family places great store on choosing a lucky day for the ceremony, so the go-between consults a priest. The bride's good luck receives no such consideration, so she may seek a glimpse into her future from a fortune teller. "A very long life, a very happy one, with many sons," she is told.

Her family's social position demands that the bride's wedding gown be the most elaborate and luxurious the family can afford. And the bride herself vows to be worthy of it! Framing her chalk-white painted face she wears a false coiffure recalling the elaborate hair styles of olden days. A white hood over the high-massed hair covers the bride's "horns of jealousy" as a symbol that never in married life will she show her jealousy to the groom. Her purse contains a good luck charm; but in case it doesn't work, she is also given a tiny ceremonial dagger.

The marriage ceremony itself is a long and complex ritual, also filled with symbolism and calculated to please the gods and the honored ancestors. The vows are sealed by the exchange of sips of sake—three sips each from each of three cups, since three is the lucky number in Japan and three times three is luckiest of all. The vows of the groom are made not to the bride but to the illustrious ancestors; so tradition is upheld.

LAND OF SEACOASTS. Though modern customs are creeping into city life, there are countless country villages of Japan where life goes on unchanged. Among these are the seacoast villages where the fishermen live.

Japan is made up of literally hundreds of small islands scattered among four larger islands. An undersea mountain range rising up from the deep floor of the Pacific Ocean thrusts its sharp peaks out of the sea to form this rugged archipelago.

So rough is the terrain of Japan that less than one-fifth of the land is suitable for cultivation. However, if Japan is short on land, she is long on coastline. And in the seas surrounding the islands the Japanese find resources to compensate for their shortage of agricultural products. Instead of meat, the Japanese eat fish. And supplying the nation's insatiable demand for seafood keeps busy an army of fishermen and their families. Let us look in upon one such fishing family to see a typical day in the lives of those who harvest the bounty of the sea.

MORNING DUTIES. The homes of these fisher-folk usually consist of one main room which also serves as bedroom. The stirring of the youngest child has the mother up with the first rays of the morning sun. Breakfast is the first order of business. Although the meals are cooked in primitive fashion over an open fire, the small kitchen area is immaculate. A pot of rice is soon steaming over the flickering flames. And its aroma arouses the rest of the family.

First daughter, Yukiko, is by proud profession an "ama," a diving girl. Head of the house is the father, Sato-san, who is the skipper of a fishing vessel. First son and second daughter have no such proud positions as yet, but there is work aplenty for them to do all the same.

A bowl of plain boiled rice all around suffices to start the family off on the long day's work. Breakfast over, father and daughter are off together to the harbor and beach; for each has an occupation, both of them dependent upon the sea.

Sato-san's boat plies the waters far offshore in quest of fish that feed in deep and distant areas. His nets are dyed indigo blue, to match the deep blue of the waters he works. Successful fishing seems to demand this camouflaging of nets. Since waters are often stained by seaweed, other fishermen may dye their nets somber brown and red. These nets are fragile and take a severe pounding from the sea, so they are constantly in need of mending. But in a Japanese fishing village, co-operation is the key to success. So Sato-san has no trouble finding willing hands to mend his nets, then to drag them down the shore and load them onto the boat. With plenty of help, Sato-san's vessel is one of the first out of the harbor in the early morning hours.

Even after the boats have departed, the beach is still aswarm with activity. For every man who goes to sea, many more engage in preparation for the day's fishing, then comb the beaches with baskets for salvage from the sea. Some are kept busy building new boats, for new craft are constantly in the making, to keep pace with increasing demands for fish.

Others manage the community food locker, a large wooden framework supporting wicker baskets in which extra fish are kept alive. Families who have good credit ratings can draw on this reserve of fresh fish in times of need. Still other villagers are kept busy drying squid on lines for use when fresh fish may be in short supply.

THE DIVING GIRLS. Here is the eldest daughter, preparing to start her day's work. She joins the other ama girls in her group in the secluded cove which serves as their headquarters. There they change clothes, hanging their land clothes on a rack, donning shorts or wrap-around skirts, with thin cotton towels around their hair. Yukiko wears a blouse too, though some of the divers prefer to go without.

Each girl takes a small net from a pole; she puts cloth "thimbles" on her fingertips as protection against rough rocks, and, with goggles to improve her underwater vision, she is ready.

Some of the ama are married to boatmen and go out as husband and wife teams. Yukiko is not married yet, but a young bachelor fisherman has

The "ama," or diving girl, puts on a face plate before diving into the cold water.

At the diving spot the ama girl tosses her barrel over the side and jumps after it.

his eye on her; for a wife who can dive is a worthwhile find, and Yukiko has been a full-fledged diver since she was fifteen. Probably, like other women of her village, she will keep on diving until she is 55 or 60, and afterward will stay ashore sorting the seaweed brought in by others.

For that is the quest of the ama—the harvesting of the seaweed called "tengus" or "heaven grass." Rich in iodine and other minerals, it is dried, baled, and then sold to factories for processing into agar-agar, a gelatinous product with many uses, an important supplement to the nation's diet.

Yukiko helps launch the boat from which she works into the tricky surf. For a few minutes then she can rest, until the boat reaches the diving spot —a jealously guarded locale. There she tosses a wooden barrel, which serves as a float for her net, over the side. Then, lowering her goggles, she jumps in after it. Where the rocks to which the seaweed clings break the surface of the sea, Yukiko may not have to go down more than a couple of feet to start finding her handfuls of seaweed. But the choicest grasses sometimes lie thirty to sixty feet under water. And one very rare type grows only in rough water, amid jagged rocks. Yukiko is sometimes willing to take the added risk of going after it, for it brings a higher price.

Down she goes, her legs waving for a moment in the air. Then she disappears under water, with only her barrel bobbing on top like a buoy to mark her dive. After almost a minute she is back, emptying her handful of seaweed into the net, then diving again.

And what of the boatman? While the ama girl clings to her floating barrel for a moment's chilly rest, breathing with sharp, whistling, open-mouthed breaths, the boatman has his fire going in a box of damp sand aboard the little boat and is cozily warming his hands while he brings a pot of tea-water to the boiling point.

No such comforts for the ama girl, whose search continues among the jagged rocks, in icy waters. Now and again she does hoist herself aboard the boat for a moment, to dry her soaking clothes. Then she pulls off the cloth thimbles to rub circulation back into her numbed fingertips. But soon she dives back to the rocky depths. For an ama can afford little time off if she's to do well at her job. One dive may net her only a small handful of the precious weed. And the season is short—from May to mid-October, with rough seas often keeping her ashore more than half of those days.

At lunch time the ama girls welcome a hearty meal and some rest and conversation.

The sun is high now; it is time to stop for lunch ashore, and after a long, hard morning's work a hearty meal is welcome. A big kettle of rice is steaming in the cove; there are raw eggs and nourishing soy bean curd, and perhaps a string of tasty sardines broiled over the open fire. The girls eat heartily. There is time for rest, too, and a bit of chatter before the boats push out into the surf again, carrying the divers back to work. Why are the boatmen not doing the diving in place of the women? Oh, they reply with a grin and a shrug, it has always been women's work.

At day's end the ama girls carry their harvest of seaweed to a central spot where it is dried. After the curing period, it is pounded and beaten by a team of women seated in facing rows, until all impurities have been removed. Then, baled and weighed, the seaweed is shipped to industrial centers, where it is processed into a gelatinous commodity rich in food value.

On her way home, at day's end, Yukiko may stroll with a friend through the village, past the open-fronted shops with their tempting assortments of goods, past the barber shop where the barber sits drowsily. When festival time comes, perhaps she herself will drop in at the barber shop; for the old-fashioned standard of Nipponese beauty demands a smooth-shaven face, from high hairline to neck, with even the eyebrows sacrificed and a coating of white powder over all.

She may pass the makers of wooden tubs for shipping fish to market, the menders of nets, the women washing clothing in the stream (unstitching kimonos for every laundering). She may pass the school where second daughter and her brother learn reading and writing—using no simple alphabet like ours of twenty-six letters, but thousands of picture-writing characters—and arithmetic on an abacus with beads to slide on wires. In deft hands this system can be as swift and certain as an electric adding machine!

THE FLEET IS IN! Down on the shore, as the day draws to its close, the watchman keeps an eye on the horizon, for the sardine fleet is due. As

The diving girls turn their seaweed over to older women, who pound it and beat it into shape.

the first ship comes into sight, the watchman pulls himself stiffly to his feet and creaks up a nearby ladder to hammer out the news on a gong suspended there.

All around the village, men in the fields straighten up and hold their stiff backs at the sound of that gong. For it is the call to more work for them; caring for the catch demands everyone's help, and no harvest is more important to the welfare of all in the village than that which comes from the sea.

So as the boats slide in toward shore, men and women together man the towlines; plodding up the beach, bent-backed, they drag the boats behind them up onto the sand. Some of the men place slippery, greased wooden frames ahead of

243

Many hands make the work easier at the turnstile, pulling in the fishing boats.

Both men and women help to pull the boats up onto the beach with towlines.

Workmen clad in rain jackets hand down baskets of fish from the laden boat.

the boats, then race around in back to pick up the skids the boat has left behind, for use again up ahead. Not until the boats are safely beached beyond the limit of the tide is their task complete.

Another crew is hauling in the drag nets, a wet and heavy task. But the heavier the net, the bigger the catch of fish, so the men do not complain as they slosh in toward shore through the light surf.

Now sardines by the basketful are taken from the nets and dumped into waiting tubs. Sardines by the tubful, the netful, the boatful, make up the bulk of the catch. But the supply can never equal the demand, for sardines by the ton are consumed daily in Japan.

With the catch packed for shipping, boat at rest in the harbor, Sato-san starts home for a little relaxation. And for pure relaxation, nothing can compare with the evening bath. While mother tends the open fire under the big stone vat, to heat the water to just below the boiling point, the rest of the family lathers and rinses thoroughly in preparation. For of course no one would take the soil of the day into the clean, hot water of the bath! At last, scrubbed clean, into the tub they go, and the soothing heat soaks away stiffness and soreness, bringing serene delight.

Then it is time for the evening meal. Since Sato-san is the skipper of a boat, he has brought home a red snapper which he caught with hook and line dropped over the side of the boat. This kind of catch is not large or of commercial importance, but it brings a nice variety into a simple meal.

The meal is not lavish, but it is sufficient, and served up with pleasant conversation—including Sato-san's tall tales of "those that got away" —it is a pleasant family time, rounding out a busy day.

A glance at the newspaper for father, a last bit of never-ending homemaking work for mother, and the quiet of night settles down once more over the village by the sea.

Tomorrow the pattern will be repeated, an age-old pattern of simple beauty, one pattern of life on the islands of Japan.

Thailand

As our airplane passes over jungle-covered mountain peaks to enter the valley of Thailand, or Siam, we are reminded of what we have heard of this small kingdom.

We have heard that Thailand is happy and peaceful. Now the first essential for happiness and calm, we know, is material security. This, in the vast stretches of Asia, means rice. And Thailand overflows with rice. Rice calls for water: water in the heavens, water on the surface of the earth, reserves of water in the hidden depths. Thailand is truly beloved of the gods, for Thailand is bathed in water.

This is what we have heard. But as our plane drops lower over the land, all we can distinguish is brown gashes in hard, dry earth. As for water in the heaven, we cannot see a mist, not even a cloud but for one small puff from a factory chimney. As for the earth, its brown color speaks of a frightful dryness. There is not a blade of grass to be seen. If we look carefully, we can see some lines of dusty green crossing this dry immensity, barely visible. All the rest is a bare desert monotone, burned by the sun.

Yes, this is really Thailand; but we have arrived a bit early, at the end of the dry season.

Also, our means of approach gives rise to false impressions. The immense flatness of the rice-fields exists, it is true, but it is the little inhabited islets and the pathways of men which attract our attention on the ground. When we travel by boat along those "almost invisible green lines" which mark the klongs, you will see that these canals provide communication between the tiny. bright spots which are villages; and you will see nothing all around you, during the journey, but trees, green growing things, and water.

THE RAINS COME. Also, you will hear the season's first rain falling on the dry jungle. Listen! For some time a singular whispering, like the murmur of a slow river, has been audible. Most certainly you can see some clouds now, far away above the mountains. The whole horizon seems to be a writhing tangle of gray and black dragons. But it does not rain.

245

The rice fields represent the source of all prosperity in Siam.

If you ask the native who comes out of the forest, he will smile and say, "The feathers of the chandrawasi are dripping." It is a legendary bird of Hindu mythology to which he refers. In his picturesque language, half-jestingly, this man is telling you that it is raining.

Raining? But we heard this same whispering a quarter of an hour ago, and we still cannot feel the smallest drop. This is because the rain can be heard a long way off, long before it reaches us, the air of Siam is so calm. There are no other sounds than those of nature. It is the distant jungle which is now receiving its first bath of the season.

The sound draws nearer though, and at last we see the rain. A gray wall has risen up to the summit of the mountains and dropped down to the plains. Behind it there is nothing; the wall of rain shuts off the sky and even the forest along our way.

Now we can distinguish the pattering on crisp leaves. The wall approaches; we are about to be soaked. We are deafened by a roaring avalanche, engulfed in a moving sea.

But this first shower does not last long. Soon it is finished. As we lift our heads, the sun shines anew. Each tree, every tuft of the jungle expresses its gratitude for heaven's blessing by exhaling a vapor whiter than snow. All the mountains smoke, and off in the forest the monkeys break into a joyous chorus of long hoots and howls.

As the days pass, the brown color vanishes from the plain. The green spots around the villages and along the klongs widen and spread over the rice fields. Thailand changes color as certain planets do under the eyes of the astronomers.

As the rains continue to fall and the river to rise, the Menam River leaves its bed; the "mother of waters" covers the rice fields, in its periodic, watched-for flood. At first glance now all we see is a lake stretching out on all sides in a water monotone, from which rise a few trees, a few houses, but which in general seems as lifeless as the desert it was before.

This is another of the optical illusions caused by taking a distant view. In the villages we find life going on at the customary pace, despite a foot of water on all the roads.

THE FLOATING CITY. But the way to see Thailand is from a sampan on the klongs. Here on either side of the canal are houses whose floors are just above the level of the water. If the river rises just a bit more, surely they will be flooded!

But no, they are built to rise with the flood. Each has a framework of big bamboos for a foundation. The Siamese of the klongs build their houses of solid teakwood, but on moving foundations.

The canals themselves are swarming with all the dizzying tumult of a floating city. Our sampan glides down the narrow, crowded canal, slipping between homes which turn open faces to the water.

Here are the shops of a market which offers fruits, fish of all sizes, a wide variety of spices, shrimps of many colors, all in a clamorous atmosphere as odorous as a pickle jar.

Many of the sampans, with their semicircular bamboo roofs, are floating homes. On them all year round live the true inhabitants of the canals. Some of them buy fruits in the country and bring them in to Bangkok to sell. One of these is the boatman Sala; his wife, with the lovely smile, is named Sawai. Their small son Pok is with them— the whole family. Their boat is laden with fruit— pineapples, golden mangoes, and others—which fill the craft with their strong aroma.

Other sampan dwellers come to make their purchases, slipping adroitly through the clogged traffic in their small canoes. The merchants shout from one bank to the other, yelling to make themselves understood.

Everyone in the Siamese family, even the small children, has a job to do aboard the sampan.

The end of the trip to the city is always a feast day, and Sawai, having stocked up from the market boats alongside, celebrates by making a big curry on her small charcoal brazier. When it is ready, the diners wash their hands, take a handful of rice in one hand, dampen it with a bit of sauce, add a bite of meat on top, and down it goes! This is the national dish of Siam. A Westerner tasting it feels as though he is on fire inside, for the sauce, which is based on creamy coconut, contains ten spices made from fiery peppers. But what an aroma drifts up from the sampan's deck to join the others hovering fragrantly over the crowded klong!

These people of the floating city do not fear the flood swelling beneath them. They move along, rising with the level of the klong, like a great Noah's ark.

Gradually the rhythm of the rains slows down. The cloudbursts give way to shorter and shorter showers. The river returns to its banks. The dwellers on the ark see their horizon lower itself a little each day. Soon one of the houses is grounded. It has to be freed with big bamboo poles acting as levers, among a chorus of cries, squeals and gibes addressed to the unlucky fellow who has destroyed the harmony of the floating city.

The mother of waters retires. This is a great day, a sign of prosperity for Thailand. Fishermen and children make a tour of the pools, vying with the birds for possession of the small fish trapped there. But for the wise farmer, fishing is a luxury, a pastime which is excusable only during the flood. Now it is time to think of a more serious matter: the rice. The good spirit of the waters has done its work; before retiring, the Menam has spread over the plain a marvelously fertile layer of silt. Now the men must do the rest—that is, the men, women and buffaloes.

THE BUFFALOS. What peaceable animals these buffaloes are! They plod along through the mud, as docile as old work horses. Some, we see, are covered with small black and white birds. These birds keep the buffaloes free from bothersome

Buffaloes, the working beasts of Siam, plod peacefully through the shallow flood waters.

insects; in the ancient folk tales they are known as doctors for the great beasts.

But surely that long brown streak on the neck of one is not a bird. No, it is a baby! Really a child of three or four years, this is the guardian of the herd. What does he do? He sits quietly; he dreams; perhaps he even thinks deep thoughts. The great philosopher Lao Tse, it is said, sat on the broad back of a buffalo while he composed his works.

Now the herd comes to a tributary of the Menam. Good heavens! See what enters the river here! The current is violent; they will be swept away. All one can see above the water are muzzles. And the child.

But we need not worry about the child. This crossing is to him an ever-fresh delight. He has awakened and now directs the maneuver with squeals of pleasure. He cries to stir up his beasts and to point out the spot on the far bank they are to reach. He does not know how to swim, but he keeps a firm grip on a horn, letting go only to seize the tail of another animal.

This is the normal way to return to the village. The herd approaches, the buffaloes stamping and snuffling, their muzzles full of slime and froth. Their backs are at the level of the water, so the boy can remount his perch without effort, astride this time. He is wide awake now, and strikes great blows on the beasts' flanks to make them quit the delights of the mud bath, where they have a tendency to loiter.

The boy maneuvers them as he pleases for

they are docile animals—unless, by chance they catch sight or whiff of an Occidental. They cannot stand Westerners, and will lower their heads and, with great scraping of the soles of their feet, charge!

At the sight of a white man scampering to escape the charging beast, the little guardian of the herd will be convulsed with laughter. He laughs openly, without any ill feeling; he wants the white man to have the pleasure of knowing what a rare spectacle he has made. He is not servile; he has a sense of humor and he does not feel that he is doing anything wrong. He is a real Thai, a free man, a true, authentic, good little Siamese.

His favorite occupation is watching the buffaloes, and you have seen how conscientiously he acquits himself. He likes this much better than helping transplant the rice.

THE KATHIN FESTIVAL. Let us leave the rice fields, for the peasants, too, are abandoning them for a few days before commencing their serious work. A grand event is being prepared for the kingdom of Siam, the festival known as Kathin.

Man in any clime does not like to approach a physical undertaking without first giving satisfaction to his spirit. This instinct the Oriental spirit expresses in the form of popular rejoicing and offerings to divine powers. The rituals are conceived as a mystical communion with the occult forces which are thought to govern the universe.

The end of the season of rains and the hope of an abundant harvest are celebrated with a great festival in all the Buddhist world; but nowhere are they celebrated with more amplitude and picturesque exuberance than in Thailand, the country of free men. This is the spectacle we wish to see.

In Bangkok, in the villages, and in the most humble country place, men and women have been absorbed for many days in elaborate preparations, decorating the altars and spending all their coins to provide suitable offerings to present to the innumerable Buddhas, to their priests and

248

to the familiar spirits. For this great festival is actually a benefit held for the temple and the priests.

Some spend their time lovingly folding bank notes into flowers. Each flower is fastened to a stalk, and all together they form a money tree which the bonzes, or monks, will collect as the climax of the ceremony. Can you imagine such a refinement of charity? Think of the value added to the money by the delicacy of the proceeding and by the amount of patience and pains taken with this work of art. In Thailand, in all things, being pleasing to the eye is felt to be as important as being useful.

When the king of Siam was one of the most powerful sovereigns of the Far East, the monarchs of Burma, Cambodia and Laos used to pay him this sort of tribute each year. It differed in only one way; it was made entirely of gold. The gold itself was not considered precious enough; it was presented in the form of a tree, with all the branches and the leaves artistically engraved.

Other marvels have been prepared, and the festival begins at sunrise. Let us follow the people as they spill out into the streets of Bangkok. They form a great wave, which parts before a rich procession. The king is leaving his palace, accompanied by dignitaries, and is going to visit the fa-

Paper money is lovingly fashioned into flowers to decorate the money tree.

mous temples of the capital, the "wats." The motley human flood flows together again behind the royal procession. Men, women and children push this way and that to be close in following.

Here is the Wat Po. Its gate is guarded by two giants leaning on their stone staffs. It contains not less than four hundred gilded statues of Buddhas, its rooms are decorated with gold and lacquer, and its spire, tapering symbol of the Buddhist faith, is covered with innumerable small yellow and green tiles off which the sun's rays glance.

Here is the Wat Chang, whose splendor is reflected in the river, and whose pure spire shoots up against a white sky, supported from below by three platforms covered with blazing porcelains of purple and blue.

Then there is the Wat Benchera, its roof of fine gold topping walls of white marble, its sides sculptured and tinted vermillion red. Its roof is covered with mosaics of which the turned-up edges are ornamented with fantastic serpents, representing the spirit of the waters.

Parchment is carefully cut and placed over the bamboo frame of the money tree.

There are not only these official monuments to be honored. Other processions stop before thousands of small, improvised temples, just as picturesque, if not as rich. Each booth is transformed into an altar or throne for a Buddha more or less grand, of material more or less precious, but always surrounded with flowers, candles, colored papers, and draperies of cloth.

The festival has no more than begun. It continues on the water, where the annual donations are celebrated. The royal procession, followed by all the people, stops at the bank of the river. On this occasion the king, though he owns a modern yacht, uses instead his ancestral boat. It is a superbly slender galley whose prow towers above the river, with a double tier of oarsmen dressed in purple. The king's throne is encrusted with gold and precious stones, and one can recognize in the slender lines of the boat the proud, slim form of the naga, the serpent-spirit of the water, which adorns the roofs of the pagodas.

The Menam is covered with thousands of boat

Every young Siamese man is expected to spend a few months in the saffron robes of a monk.

launchings and the whole population of Bangkok rows toward the sea in the retinue of their king, a flotilla made up of a strange assortment of elements. There are Siamese sampans, Chinese junks, some Malayan "praus," boats of all styles, their prows carved and painted in bright colors. Some children have made use of their little canoes. Some familes of land-dwellers have made rafts of bamboo and follow the parade.

The armada is constantly being enlarged by new additions. At evening they arrive at the mouth of the river. It is here that they have built on an island the great pagoda of Pak-Nam, in which the principal religious festival will unfold. The king steps ashore and is welcomed into the temple by silent, reserved priests. Behind him, the thousands of pilgrims vie for landings. It is not easy. The boats bump; the rafts collide; in the tangle, some of the boatsmen are injured. The fever mounts around the sacred temple. The island is surrounded by a swaying wreath of overlapping boats, all swarming with life, and full of a rising sound of excitement.

Night arrives. The temple itself is aglow, its long galleries lighted by a multitude of candles. The priests push open the doors. The throng is finally admitted to the interior, and calm settles over them as they penetrate more deeply into the sanctuary. It is finally in a religious silence that they march forward and place their offerings before the great Buddha.

But out-of-doors the festival lasts all night, both on land and on the water, attaining at times a kind of frenzy. Bursts of fireworks light the scene. The carvings and the gilt glitter under bursts of Bengal light. Garlands of lanterns are glowing on the island and on the boats. This city of a single night scintillates as if in the grip of a fever.

It is a city with its merchants ever on the alert, taking advantage of the mounting excitement to peddle their wares. Not all are pilgrims of the faith on this expedition! The Chinese and Moslems, too, have come down the Menam with their little floating shops supplying food, beverages, painted papers, sticks of incense, amulets and charms, images of Buddha.

A Kathin priest stands in the courtyard of his elaborate temple.

This is a city with its section of cabarets, its theater where the actors contort themselves, where professional dancers mimic religious scenes; with its public places where other dancers improvise, imitating to the best of their ability the gestures of the experts; with its fakirs and its readers of horoscopes—a city whose enthusiasm explodes at every instant with odd inventions. See these boats, which the young men launch into the current after setting them afire, and which collide with each other, showering cascades of sparks, to the accompaniment of applause and the stamping of feet.

Take one last look at this fairy scene, for the sun is rising to the gilded summits of the temple spires, and this is the signal for breaking up. The boats go slowly back up the river to their villages or to the capital. Bodies are weary and spirits satisfied. The rice crop of Siam should grow well.

SIAMESE BUDDHISM. Perhaps this Buddhist festival surprises you with its splendor and exuberance, its dances, its joyous feasting, its enthusiasm rising to delirium, its clear display of love of beauty, material pleasures and nature—in a word, its passion for life. Perhaps you have thought of Buddhism as an abstract religion without a god or heavenly creature, whose followers preach isolation, dependence on oneself, renouncement of the joys of the world and disregard for any kind of material pleasure. The supreme Good of pure Buddhism consists in total annihilation, after a series of earthly existences both wearisome and sad.

In Siam the priests practice the pure doctrine of Buddhism. In their yellow robes, with shaven heads, uncovered shoulder, bare feet, they stand apart from the exuberance of the festival and live according to the precepts of the Sage. They meditate. They do not kill any animals. They live modestly on charity. And every male is expected to spend at least three months of his life in the priesthood.

As for the people, they have chosen among the angels and demons of all races those which suit their temperament. The demons we see guarding the thousands of gilded Buddhas, those monstrous statues of stone, are from an old mythology. They are "yaks," found in every temple of the realm, and the more revered the sanctuary is,

251

movements of the feminine body express the mystic emotions of a religion which scorns the body and disdains women. The dancers are chosen very young, for their beauty and suppleness. They spend their lives in cultivating the expressiveness of their bodies, on which they impose a range of special and sensual undulating movements in which their whole being takes part, to the very tips of their ornamented fingers. To give still greater value to their postures, they appear in sumptuous costumes and their every quiver sets a cascade of gold and precious jewels to sparkling and glittering.

How is this dance interpreted? It is a visit to paradise. The richness of the rhythmic vibration of lovely bodies lavishly displaying the excitement of life calls up a vision of paradise—that paradise which consists in motionlessness, the annihilation of all desire, of joy, of pain, of life! Surely this is a paradox.

VARIED BANGKOK. It seems that such a conglomeration of superstitions must betray a rather backward state. Yet the airport of Bangkok is one of the best equipped in the Far East and offers most efficient service. To this realm, visitors are welcomed with a smile. Not only has Siam been a leading country in aviation, but her express trains compare in comfort with famous trains of Europe and America; her boulevards are traveled by handsome automoblies; in Bangkok's fashionable quarter, homes of brick and stone stand in the midst of fine gardens. The young wear European clothes, they may study at one of two universities, and often speak English, French—or both.

But Bangkok has other curiosities which have not been unveiled. There is also a market on land, of which you hear echoes at a distance. This is the spot for fabrics. They are heaped up on boards in all the shops and also in the open air. Merchants and buyers discuss the various colors

the more diabolic their aspect. Those faces, part man, part beast, those menacing fangs and those nightmare grins quiet the doubts of mistrustful Siamese. Only here will you find side by side worrisome and malicious demons, Chinese dragons, Burmese gnomes, Singhalese monsters, disembodied spirits from Malaya, all the thousands of spirits to whom the mysteries of nature have given rise in the imagination of the countries of the Orient. Adopted through the course of ages by the welcoming Siamese people, they threaten to trouble the quiet "nirvana" of the Sage—that Buddhist world-to-come which does not admit any occult power.

As for the sacred dances, they are a part of any religious festival of importance. The graceful

Boatloads bound for the festival buy temple offerings at these floating shops.

Boatloads bound for the festival buy temple offerings at these floating shops.

at length. Thousands of curious and feverish hands touch them, unfolding and crushing the lovely goods.

See the black Tamils who praise their Indian prints and saris. See the Bengalis who sell cloth to the peasants of the rice fields, silk sarongs to the Malayans and sampots to the Cambodians. The Chinese offer porcelains of their country, Japanese screens, Javanese daggers, Persian carpets, and bric-a-brac in tin and bronze. There are Burmese who display stones, more or less precious but all brilliant in color. Along comes a priest in his yellow robe, holding out one side of his cloak to protect him from the touch of women and at the same time half opening his robe to show the bowl in which he receives his offerings. Here are Laotians who sell fish from large baskets of reeds. Along the most odorous of the canals of the city are the miserable Chinese shops in wretched shanties. Yet some of their owners possess the greatest fortunes and the richest villas in all of Siam.

Finally, here is the district, by far the cleanest, where the small craftsmen work. Objects of engraved metal (the niello, an alloy of copper and silver skillfully proportioned and fired in a kiln)

Coolies of many different nationalities are the burden-bearers of Siam.

Musical instruments come in many strange and wondrous shapes and sizes in Siam.

The hard-working elephant and his mahout spend much of their lives together.

she combines art and industry, usefulness and elegance, grace and ingenuity—in her person as well as in her work. It would not surprise us if she has a bit of Chinese blood, for through the years there has been much mixing of the races. And from these marriages has been born a race at once strong and graceful, whose members adopt the nationality and customs of Thailand.

CHANG THE ELEPHANT. Let us leave the great city of Bangkok for the high regions, cradle of the Thai race, the country of elephants and great forests of teak. Five hundred miles north of Bangkok, in the mountains near Burma, you will be able to watch Chang the elephant at work with his indispensable keeper, the "mahout."

Perhaps you have seen a caterpillar tractor, equipped with a bulldozer blade and run by a skilled operator, when the machine encountered an obstacle that resisted it. At the first contact with the resisting mass, the machine gives the impression of a living creature, tensing its muscles to the limit of its strength. The operator, bouncing on his seat, manipulates his controls with a nervous hand, constantly varying the power of the motor and working his feet on the pedals. His intelligence and his nerves are sinews of the great brute. His frowning face reflects each reaction of the machine to the obstacle. In a fraction of a second, his spirit loses itself in compensating for the errors and lacks of blind energy, holding the brute to the task.

The mahout works in just the same way with the five tons of meat and muscle which he commands by touches on sensitive points of the elephant's skin. It is thought-demanding work, like that of the "cat" driver, but it also calls for the

are a Siamese art. The designs are of remarkable delicacy, for the Siamese are masters of the art of working precious metals.

Here a graceful young lady paints flowers on a parasol with both care and taste. The design is of fine quality, but her method is even more interesting, for she spreads several colors at the same time with a single brush stroke. Her fingers are deft, her air is concentrated. How happily

Teak logs must be left in the sun for a year or more, until they are dry enough to float.

participation of the whole body. When they stop, the mahout is streaming with sweat, like the elephant. We must give each an equal share in the credit for moving the great trunks. And an equal share in the responsibility, too. That was the Siamese view, not so very long ago.

In certain cases (very rare, because the elephant is generally docile, attached to its keeper, and well treated) there are conflicts of personality. That can end badly for the mahout. He is thrown from his seat by a stroke of the trunk, tossed in the air and mashed into pulp when he falls to the ground.

The wise old Siamese law ordained that the beast then be tried. He might have had an excellent reason for the killing. If it was proven that the elephant had been mistreated, the tribunal decided that this was legitimate self-defense and acquitted him. He took up his duties again with a new servant—almost always more understanding, Siamese chroniclers remark. If, on the contrary, the debate revealed that he acted without provocation, he was condemned and put to death. The Buddhist philosophy gave the animal a chance equal to that of a man; and if you reflect for a moment, you will agree that it was a reasonable view of the situation.

In Burma, Malaya and Indochina, elephants have been decimated by hunters, but in Siam they are protected. No elephants are considered "wild" in Siam; the herds in the jungle are considered the property of the state, and it is forbidden to kill them. The raids of which one hears were not really hunts and did not end in massacres. Of the number which were captured, ten or so were kept, usually the youngest. The rest, given their liberty, returned to the jungle.

Nowadays, the use of elephants is becoming more rare. The Siamese, who may seem backward and naive, decided at the beginning of the century that their natural teak forests would soon

be exhausted if they continued cutting them down. So they planted vast stretches of artificial forests. Moreover, they chose terrain that was easily reached and left great openings which permit the use of mechanical equipment. So while the supply of precious teak has all but disappeared in the surrounding countries, Thailand today has great plantations equipped with modern tractors. On these, elephants are used only as helpers. Still, though the mahout dates back to another age, you may be sure that he will be able to do in days many things a bulldozer will take weeks to do. Tractors will not entirely replace the elephant.

From the forest or plantation, the road of the teak leads down the Menam to Bangkok. But it takes some logs as much as eight years to reach the port.

Here is a lumber camp. The lumbermen kill but do not cut down the trees. They make an incision with an ax all around the trunk. The tree dies in forty-eight hours. But they will not cut it down until a year later, and then it will dry in the sun for a second year. The Siamese have patience; but also, the wood when green is too heavy to float.

At last the logs are pushed into the river, which here in the uplands glides between two

A cool bath is a welcome treat for an elephant after a long, hard day's work.

compact masses of jungle. It is as clear and glittering as an Alpine torrent—and scarcely larger. The logs ram themselves into rocks in the rapids along the winding river; sometimes they are grounded and are freed only by the next flood; but finally they arrive at the landing place.

Where the Menam broadens, leaves the forest and becomes a real river flowing out upon the plain, there is the first landing place of the teak. At this stop the wood of several years is assembled into immense rafts. The hazardous rapids are passed, and steered navigation is now possible. The raft train with the boatmen's houses on top keeps to the middle of the river. And for some months during the voyage the men live in a little

hamlet peacefully drifting downstream toward Bangkok, with little to do but watch the crocodiles sunning themselves on the banks.

At last they are down in the swirling current near the capital. The klongs increase in numbers on either bank, and pour out sampans into the Menam. We are back again among the water dwellers, who are living symbols of Siam. For kings will come and kings will go; great temples will rise only to crumble into dust. But as long as the rivers rise in their season to flood the land with richness, these people will endure. And the priceless gift of happiness will continue to be their reward for having learned to live in harmony with the friendly floods of Thailand.

After months in the back country, the busy klongs are a welcome sight to the Siamese.